Published by Leaf by Leaf Press 2019
www.leafbyleafpress.com

Copyright © Vicky Turrell 2019

Vicky Turrell has asserted her right to be identified as the author
of this work in accordance with the Copyright, Design and
Patents Act 1988

ISBN 978-1-9993122-2-0

This story was inspired by real events although some scenes and people
have been invented for the purpose of the narrative. My mother's
thoughts and words are from my own imagination. Any medical
information in this book is based solely on the author's experience and
should not be used as a substitute for professional advice.

Printed and bound in Great Britain by Clays Ltd, Elcograf S.p.A.

My mother said –
'When you are my age, you will understand.'

Acknowledgements

I would like to thank members of Oswestry Writers Group for all their encouragement and comments – special thanks to Ian Malcolm for his help in finding a context for my mother's life and times. Thank you also to the members of Leaf by Leaf Press who have given me constant support and appraisal – special thanks to Bernard who helped me find my mother's voice and to John who worked on the script to prepare it for printing.

Thank you to those individuals who have kindly shared, with me, their knowledge and experience of Parkinson's disease. Also, I am grateful to the staff at Kingston Theatre Hotel, who showed me where my mother worked when the building was Madame Clapham's.

My thanks also go to Helen Baggott for her expert editing and understanding.

Me and my Mam

By
Vicky Turrell

Chapter 1

Trapped

Me

I think that my mam poisoned me when I was a baby. Nothing was ever said to me, of course, but I think it was true. I was her third baby girl and I expect she and Dad wanted a boy to help run our farm when he was older. She already had two girls and wouldn't like another.

I could tell that Mam didn't like the fortune teller, either, because when she came to the door, Mam couldn't wait to get rid of the old woman.

It happened one day, when Mam was washing our stone floor, that an old woman walked down our lane. She looked like a bundle of rags with a scarf tied round her fuzzy hair. I was outside in our orchard with Gwendy, we followed her and saw her knock on our door. Mam opened the door in surprise.

Nobody knocked on our door – they just walked in shouting, "It's only me," and we knew who it was by their voice and by the time and by the day of the week. Everything was always the same at our house. But today things were different because of this old woman.

"Tell your fortune, dearie," she said. She wasn't from round here then, nobody said 'dearie'; if they called you anything, they called you 'love'.

"No thank you," said Mam, all tight lipped and prim and proper, wiping her wet hands on her pinny.

Our Gwendy and me both gawped at the fortune teller's back. Then our Katy, home for a day from her nursing in Hull, came from our room with a duster in her hand to see what was going on.

"You have three girls, dearie."

I wasn't sure whether that was the fortune telling, or just saying what she saw. Mam didn't say anything but pushed a loose lock of her permed hair behind her ears and looked at the woman with pursed lips.

"One daughter is very hard working.

One is very beautiful.

One is very like you."

The folds of dark material hung around her in flaps, like our broken umbrella. Her elbows were tightly tucked in, so you could hardly see her weather-brown hand when it peeped out, palm upwards. I expect she wanted some money, but Mam said very politely, "No thank you," and then she closed the door with a snap. Me and Gwendy stood there on the outside with the woman. She didn't move for a minute, then she scuttled off next door.

"Tell your fortune, dearie," she said to Aunty Vera.

"Oh, come in, love," said Aunty Vera and scooped up the bundled woman and then, huddled together, they went inside. I was sure that they would sit by the fire, which I knew would be roaring with logs. Me and Gwendy went in to see how they were getting on after a few minutes, and there was the woman, sitting in a chair near the fire, with her brown peeping-out hands hugging a steaming mug of tea. Grandma sat bolt upright in her chair on the other side, away from the fire. She was staring into the distance with a face looking like she'd eaten a sour damson from our orchard. She was moving her lips, like our cows do when they chew their cud, and I knew that meant that she wasn't pleased.

Aunty Vera knelt on their coconut mat – it was all wrinkly and hard like Grandma's face. We sat down next to her and stared with open mouths. I could see Aunty Vera's soft white bosoms diving into her tight red jumper. They looked so lovely and comfy I wanted to dive down with them and snuggle up right there and then. But I didn't, of course, we were all concentrating on the fortune teller.

2

"I can see great changes ahead for all of you, with lots of important decisions to be made." Well that was pretty boring, I was thinking of going off to find the other kids and see if they wanted to play a game.

"You will have a new man in your life, dearie, he will appear when you least expect him, so be on your guard." A new man? Aunty Vera already had Uncle Sid — why would she want a new man? Aunty Vera gasped, and we copied her, Grandma sniffed and chewed her cud even more.

The fortune teller got up to go, and Aunty Vera went to get her purse and gave her a shilling. I could see Aunty Vera's hand was trembling a bit with excitement. The woman's hand gripped the coin tightly, then it disappeared into her flurry of shawls.

Mam's hand was trembling a bit as well when she was dishing up our tea of liver and onions. I wonder if she was thinking about her father, who was poorly. Or maybe it was the fortune teller she was thinking about, well, you couldn't help but think about her really, could you?

Who was the hard working one of us three girls? Who was the pretty one? Who was the special one that was just like Mam?

I didn't know which one to choose — I wanted to be hard working because I wanted to get on in the world, but our Katy worked harder than me. She had a job in Hull and she came to help Mam with housework.

I did want to be very beautiful, of course I did. But our Gwendy wanted to be beautiful as well because she was getting ready to enter Ringam beauty competition. You had to go to the dances every week on a Saturday night and Mam said that these were called preliminary dances, and then she said that you could get selected by the important men who spotted your potential.

Gwendy tried very hard and every night she was sitting at Mam's three-way mirror, in their bedroom combing her hair and trying on Mam's lipstick. Then she started going to the dances on a Saturday night with Mam and Dad at the village hall in Ringam.

I stayed at home and read our comics in bed. Then I switched the light off and stared into the blackness waiting for our van's headlights to come searching down our lane and swish round our bedroom wall. When I saw that light, I knew they were all back home safely and I went to sleep straight away and didn't even hear our Gwendy coming into the bed next to me. Everything was safe and the same as it always had been.

Well, in the morning I heard that our Gwendy got chosen, so they must have spotted her 'potential'. Now she had to think about her dress for the finals, but she didn't really have to think about it much – Mam had to think about it more, because she would be making it.

After Mam had helped with the milking and the cleaning of the cowsheds and the house, we had our dinner. We ate it in a rush because we were going on the bus to Ripsea to the remnant shop. Us kids secretly called it 'Rag Shop' because it was a bit mucky and had all sorts of bits and pieces and scraps of material.

"We are going to get some suitable material for our Gwendy's beauty contest dress," said Mam. I liked blue and Mam liked blue, but our Gwendy wanted red, and Mam said it was Gwendy's dress, so red it was. The shop was a real mess as it always was, and the sales lady was having a mug of tea, so she made one for us all. Mam fiddled among piles of remnants on the shelves and then with the scraps on the floor, then she found an end-of-roll piece of satin brocade that she reckoned she could manage, with a few hidden joins, to make into a dance dress. It cost half a crown which was a lot of money, when you think about it, because it was such a little piece of cloth. Gwendy liked its deep red pattern with silver threaded leaves and had already decided she wanted it. The shop lady said it was sophisticated and the colour of rubies, so it was settled, and Mam paid for it.

We went back on the bus to our lane end. Mam was in a rush again because she wanted to get changed in time to make our tea and then get on with the evening milking with Dad. Then, at night, she wanted to make a start on Gwendy's dress.

Well, the dress was beautiful and there was a surprise because there was more material than Mam thought (or Mam was even cleverer at sewing than I thought) and she had made a little bolero to go with it. That would keep our Gwendy warm because the dress was strapless, and her bust had to hold it up. I hadn't got any sign of a bust yet, but I didn't want to think about that, and, in any case, it was Sunday and I was off to Ringam, on the bus, to go to Sunday school.

After Sunday school, I walked with my cousin Suzy to my granddad's house. He was my mam's father and we had to go and see him because he had a disease where he couldn't go out.

"It is a terrible condition," said Mam. He daren't go out of his front door, if he tried to get out, he went up to the door and took hold of the handle and then sort-of got stuck. His hand froze on the metal and would not move, he just stood there like a statue. Then after about an hour, he had to give up and go and sit down in his chair near the fire again. And so, he didn't see anybody if we didn't go. He just sat there ripping up newspaper into long strips and then making spills to poke in the fire and light his pipe with. Then, after hours of rolling spills he went to the kitchen and rolled dough to make some biscuits.

He had been poorly with another disease in the last few weeks, but he was pleased to see us, and he had made us some munchy biscuits and there was some fizzy pop for us to drink, like there always was. I expected that his son, my Uncle Tom, had bought it for us, riding to the shops on his motorbike because Granddad, of course, couldn't go to the shops. He couldn't go anywhere. Mam said that it probably came on when his wife died so early, and he didn't cope, what with having so many children to look after. That was when my mam had to give up her embroidery work in Hull to look after everybody. I expect she was glad not to have to go on the bus to work so early in the morning. I also think that she wouldn't mind looking after them because she loved her little sisters and brothers very much – you could tell because she always smiled when she saw them or talked about them, even though they were grown up now.

She smiled at our Gwendy as well, when she saw her in her competition dress. It was perfect, tight fitting in the bodice and a full swirly skirt that shot out, like a not broken umbrella, when Gwendy gave us a twirl. They were both looking forward to that dance.

But Dad didn't want to go, he had some pigs farrowing and he wanted to be there with them, just in case the sows laid on the babies, when they had been born.

"Oh, come on, love, you can't let Gwendy down. She has been looking forward to this dance and a chance to win the beauty competition," pleaded Mam.

"I can't help that, I didn't know pigs were going to farrow tonight, did I?"

So, in the end it was agreed that Mam and Gwendy would go on the bus and Dad would join them as soon as he could, and then bring them back at the end of the dance. Gwendy and Mam started to get ready – oh, it took such a long time, they washed and set their hair and then put on dresses and then put on make -up. At the end they sprayed their special scent, called 'Ashes of Violets' everywhere.

Gwendy looked fantastic. Then, they went stepping out carefully in their high heels in between the lumps of muck on our path and yard – they wouldn't want to get any on their shoes. The judges would mark Gwendy down for that.

I got into bed and then read comics as usual – Dad was already in the pigging sheds looking after his squealing sows – it was hours before I heard him set off in our van in a big hurry to get to Ringam before it was too late. He hadn't had time to come upstairs to get changed, because his pigs needed him so much.

I heard our van going up our lane with its engine breathing its gear changes, until it turned onto the main road to Ringam, and then it faded away. I was in my bed staring at the darkness again, waiting for the headlights to flash round our bedroom. After a long time, I did see the lights, and then I knew they were all safely home. I fell asleep straight away without waiting for Gwendy's news.

I heard all the news, when I woke up in the morning, from Mam.

"Gwendy won the beauty competition last night." You could tell that she was very pleased indeed because our Gwendy won.

"She had her photo taken for the *Holderness Gazette*, wearing her ruby red brocade dress and a crown on her head. I shouldn't wonder if she isn't on the front-page next week."

Our Gwendy must be the beautiful one, then. And so, there was only one choice left from the fortune teller, I was the one daughter that was very like Mam.

I didn't think that I could be that one. But I wanted to try and be that special daughter that the fortune teller had talked about. I was thinking in bed what I could do to make this come true, when I heard a motorbike come into our yard. I jumped out of bed and stood on the windowsill, just in time to see Uncle Tom rushing to our door. Our Gwendy did the same. We stood listening, but we could only hear whispers, it was Mam and Uncle Sid, in our passage.

In the morning when we went downstairs Mam said, "Your granddad crossed over last night." She just said it without looking at us, she was putting our fried eggs on our plates for breakfast. She would be sad because it was her dad. I couldn't help being sad that there would be no more homemade biscuits for me and no more fizzy pop on a Sunday. No more 'must stay at home' Granddad, who sat near the fire tearing newspapers.

My mam was upset for a few days, I could see her face looking like Grandma's, as if she had eaten a sour damson as well, and you could hear a tremble in her voice but I wanted everything to be safe and just the same as it always was, even though we had to be without the homemade biscuits.

I didn't go to the funeral, well nobody asked me, but this time Mam did get Dad to go with her in his best funeral suit. They weren't away long though, because they had to get on with the farm work, which didn't stop just because my granddad had died.

Now, you might think that Uncle Sid and Mam had been whispering about Granddad dying and didn't want us kids to know straight away, but it was not that, because the next night when I was in bed, I heard Uncle Sid's footsteps coming into our house and there was loads more whispering. Maybe it was about Aunty Vera's new man.

I sometimes came downstairs in my nighty and pressed my ear to the stair door, but I could never tell what they were saying. The whispering went on so fast and so quietly and the mystery was still a secret.

"Wsss, wsss, wsss."

Mam

That fortune teller was just a silly woman, anybody could see that I had three girls, and she obviously just made up all that about how different they were. I don't believe in that sort of thing. Nobody can tell the future, can they? I certainly could not have foretold that I would have ended up here on this isolated farm, down a long lane with flat land as far as you could see. As for Vera having a new man in her life, well, how could she? We are both here, working all hours.

All I really want to do is my embroidery, I do it whenever I can. I learnt to embroider from my dear mother. My sisters can embroider, as well, but for me it is a passion, once I started doing it, I could not stop. When we were young, we learnt to embroider, by watching and stitching with Mother every afternoon. Now, I still stitch if I can., not out of habit but out of love.

I met Herb at a dance in the village hall. I first saw him with another girl. I knew of her, she was from a farm, a big farm, so she would be quite well to do. She was taller than Herb, he was quite short really, for a man. Then one day, he was not with her and came to ask me to dance. After that, we watched out for each other on Saturdays and we danced well together.

Then about a year later, we were walking out on the promenade at Ripsea when he asked me to marry him.

"Mebbie we should get married?" he said.

"Yes," I said.

It was as simple as that. I didn't think too long about it. I could not turn down a man like him. He and his brother worked on a farm, which had rich clay land, and a big house, so everybody thought that I had done well for myself. We got engaged.

"We'll go to Ripsea to the Holderness Jewellers and get a ring," said Herb. But it was a long time before we went.

"When are we getting that ring, Herb?" I kept asking. "Nobody believes we are engaged, we need a ring to prove it." Eventually, I gave up, then one day Sid came up to us.

"How's tricks? Have you got that ring yet? You need to make an honest woman of her, Herb," he joked.

We went on the bus to Ripsea, there was only one a day and it didn't stay long before it returned. That suited Herb because he wanted to be back working on the farm.

We had to make a decision quickly, it was a good job that there wasn't much to choose from. There were only five rings to look at, but they were all beautiful. Herb chose a ring with three bright diamonds; I had never owned anything like it. I daren't look at the price. I tried it on, and it was too big.

"That can soon be adjusted, madam," said the jeweller. "Come back next week and it will be ready."

"Drat." I was disappointed, because I wanted to wear it straight away and show everybody, but I had to wait.

"All things come to them that wait," said Herb, when he saw how I did not want to take it off, and how disappointed I was to leave it on the black velvet tray in the shop.

But I was engaged at last, and that beautiful ring would soon be on my finger. I felt like I was floating on air. I wanted to go back in the shop and say, 'It doesn't matter if it won't fit, I will take it now.' But I knew that would be silly.

"I feel so lucky, Herb, thank you." We went out of the shop and I looked out at a sparkling street – it looked like the promised land. All the colours of the houses and the trees seemed unreal and bright – they were not the same dull colours as when we went in.

We went back after a week. My ring was ready. It was in its box – a red leather box with a red velvet lining. We walked to the prom and Herb went down on one knee and I held out my left hand and he put the ring on. It fitted perfectly. All the same exciting feelings came back, and the sea seemed bright blue and the sand so perfectly white.

I rushed home to show Mother my ring. "I am so happy," I laughed.

"Calm down, Girly." She always called me 'Girly'; I don't know why. "Let's hope he treats you as well as your father treats me – then you will be very lucky indeed."

It was true, my father always treated Mother like royalty. She was used to a rich life and had learnt all the things a lady learns – like embroidery and playing the piano. She sat doing her embroidery every afternoon and played the piano in the evenings. Father even bought her a pony and trap with red velvet seats. Every week he took her round the village in it, so the villagers could see how beautiful she was.

I felt truly beautiful too, when Herb came the next week with a gold watch for me.

"It's too much," I said. "I have your beautiful ring." But Herb wanted me to have it.

"I want you to have it, as a present for my beautiful fiancée." I was on cloud nine.

But now, I had to come down to earth and think about that beauty competition, instead of my engagement so long ago. I had to hurry and get Gwendy's dress made so she could wear it for the finals. I could not help wondering, despite myself, if that fortune teller meant Gwendy when she said about one of the daughters being beautiful.

Before I was married, people always used to say how striking looking I was, with my glossy dark hair and round face and dimpled cheeks, so maybe Gwendy took her looks from me.

I wished that I could have entered a beauty competition, when I was young. It makes me so happy that Gwendy can do this. It helps me cope with the sadness of my father's illness.

Well, really, he had gone a long time ago – into his shell and he could not get out. He lived all those wasted years sitting by the fire. And after I was married, I didn't go to see him as much as I should have done. You would think that I would have learnt a lesson after Mother died, wouldn't you? All the things I wish I had said. All the kind actions I could have done. I stupidly thought that there was plenty of time, but there never is.

'How are you today, Dad?' I could have asked. We could have sat together and had a cup of tea. But I did not have that sort of time to spare and then suddenly it was too late.

When the finals for Gwendy's competition came, Herb didn't want to go.

"Please come to the dance and watch Gwendy in the beauty competition," I begged. He did not come, though.

"And the winner is our Gwendy here, and what a beauty she is," shouted the compere.

I danced with her then, round and round the dance floor we swished. I wore the green silk dress I had made for myself, our skirts fanned out as we swirled faster and faster and everybody was watching. I loved competitions and we had won, and I bathed in the glory – the beautiful mother of the winner. A beautiful daughter in her red dress.

Of course, Herb came for us in our van. I had been trying to persuade Sid to make sure Herb came in the car, but I knew it was hopeless.

Then Vera gave birth to another baby boy. I wonder if this was the new man that the fortune teller was talking about. But what am I thinking? I know that was nonsense. Vera had three boys now, to help carry on the farm and I had none. I cannot compete with Vera on that score, that is one competition I did not like. Vera was kept busy with her four children – she had a little girl called Bonny, in between the boys – just to complete their happiness.

My last baby was a girl and that was that. I had to get on with it and just accept it. People said that there could be another and it could be a boy, but I do not think I could go through all that again. Especially as my last one was so sickly.

I often wonder about that poisoning, you know. I only rubbed a small amount of teething powder on her gums. How was I to know it would harm her? The specialist said that she had Pink Disease from the teething powder, and it was up to me whether she lived or died. I do not like to think about it, even now.

But I did whisper to Sid about our situation – their three boys and us with three girls. What would happen to the farm, as they grew up? What would happen to Herb and me and our girls?

Aunty Vera's new man.
By the author (age 14)

Chapter 2

Getting on

Me

When I first went to Ripsea Comprehensive School I was so pleased to follow my teacher, Mr Fishwick, down that smart corridor. We went through the door, following two by two. Left right, left right, marching after our new form teacher. On and on we went out onto paths, marching through neatly cut grass. We followed Mr Fishwick until we turned a corner and saw some old huts.

I was pleased to see these huts, though some people might not have been. But you see, I had been to the huts at my primary school and they were wonderful. My friend Brenda and me had wandered about in the old gardens and discovered birds' nests and our teacher's bee hives. We learnt all we could about birds and bees, and I loved the old huts, so I didn't mind one little bit when we marched up to these old army huts at Ripsea school.

But I was disappointed, because these were different. There was no garden for a start, our huts at our primary school had gardens and we could run wild in them and do as we pleased. We could watch birds building their nests and we could watch our teacher's bee hive, and at a safe distance we stared at his bees buzzing in and out of the flowers. I never did quite trust those bees, even though they landed on our teacher and didn't sting him. I thought that they might sting me. You can't be too careful, can you? And I didn't quite trust these huts here, at my new school. These weren't the old huts that I knew and loved. Also, our teacher, Mr Fishwick, was not as kind as my primary school teacher, Mr Grey.

Mr Fishwick was so very strict, and we had to line up in the order of our height, outside our hut door. I was the shortest and I had to stand at the back of the line. I was little for my age because of my poisoning. Mam said that when I was a baby I didn't grow as fast as the other kids, but I had never thought much about that before. I never had to be at the back of the queue at Ringam Primary, but here at Ripsea I had to sit at the back of the classroom as well, and it was lucky that I was still good at seeing things at a distance, so I could read what Mr Fishwick was writing on the black board.

He was writing our timetable, telling us where we had to go and what we had to do every day of the week. Every hour of every day was ordered. There would be no doing as you pleased at these huts watching the birds and the bees. For a start, we had to go to assembly, which we never had to do at Ringam huts. We had to line up again in height order. That would not have been so bad, but we had to get to the main building in time for assembly, so we had to run. I was no good at running and I dropped behind, and Mr Fishwick shouted me to "Hurry along, there."

My heart was hammering, and I had to walk instead of run, and I got further and further behind. They all had to wait for me outside the hall and nobody was very pleased seeing me walking and holding up the queue.

I was glad when it was home time, but it was no good talking to Mam about the things I was not happy about, she would just tell me that I had to get on with it.

"I'm fed up," I said to Mam once.

"You'll have to get fed down, then," she said. There was nothing to be done to change what was happening at school, but I wished that I could alter what was happening to Mam at home. She didn't seem very well – she looked pale and kept on going to bed early, or sleeping near the fire in her horse hair chair, and often when she got up, she was sick. I could hear her retching in our wash house or just outside the door on our cobbles. I didn't hear her sewing machine any more either. Maybe she didn't have as much to sew now us girls were growing up and our Katy had left home to work in Hull as a nurse. But there was another thing – I didn't hear her piano playing when I was in bed.

No notes danced up to my bedroom at night. It was all very sad. But she still went out to do the milking, every morning and every night – well, she had to really, nothing was more important, we needed the milk cheques every week. She just had to get on with it all. If she was fed up, she just had to get fed down. Music could wait, and clothes could wait but our cows being milked, couldn't wait.

Ripsea school could not wait either and the time at home hurried on, and soon I was getting up again the next morning, to catch the bus.

"Girls queue up by the door," said Mr Fishwick, it was height order, of course. We marched to the main building and then we were taken, by a prefect, to the girls' toilets where the deputy head was waiting for us.

"Now you are young ladies," she whispered, "it is time for you to know about this special toilet." She pushed the door open of the cubicle at the end of the row and there was a metal box on the wall with an electric switch glowing red. There was a smell too, a frightening body burning smell. There was a little piece of grey ash on the floor, like a dead leaf.

"You must come here for the disposal," she said. We all stood staring in silence. She opened a little drawer under the metal box. We all stared in silence again.

"If you do not know what I mean, you must ask your mothers when you get home." And that was the end of that.

When I got home, I asked Mam about that cubicle toilet with the metal box. Mam still wasn't looking very well, and she was making an apple pie and was trying to get it ready before she went out milking. She smiled a pretend smile.

"Oh," she said and kept on making crumbs for her pastry, her fingers getting busier and busier by the second.

"Oh," she said again. "I thought you knew." I stood there looking at her fingers still working busily, although you couldn't get that flour and lard crumblier if you tried. I said nothing.

"Oh... well," she muttered into her bowl. "Well, you know about the birds and the bees, don't you?" Yes, I knew about the birds and the bees, I learnt about them in kind Mr Grey's class, at my primary school. I was always looking for birds' nests and Mr Grey was always telling us how to look after his bees that were in a hive just outside our class window. I knew about birds and bees alright.

"Well then..." said Mam adding water to her crummiest crumbs you ever did see. "And you know about Mrs Fox having a baby, don't you?" I couldn't see what Mrs Fox had to do with anything. She had married Mr Fox and then had a baby. So?

The pastry lumped up into a ball and she tipped it out onto her baking board and cut it in half then she banged it flat with her rolling pin, flatter and flatter it went – she was concentrating for all she was worth, but I knew that she had done this hundreds of times and didn't need to even think about what she was doing.

Bang! went her rolling pin again and she made two flat pieces, one lined the dish, then in went the cut apples with some sugar and the second piece of pastry made the lid. She pierced the crust with her knife – twice to make two slits, like she always did, and she shoved the pie in the oven. I said nothing, and Mam said, "Well then... that's alright then." And she took her pinny off and she ran outside, and I heard her being sick on our cobbles.

I knew though, that it wasn't alright. What did my birds and bees have to do with that toilet at the end of that awful corridor? And what did they have to do with Mrs Fox having a baby?

Then one day, Mam was so poorly that she couldn't get out of bed and our Katy had to come home from Hull to look after her, and it wasn't even the weekend.

Then Dr Moon was sent for from Ringam. There was no time to clean the whole house, like Mam usually does for the

Doctor, but our Katy did her best and managed to put the gold bedspread on Mam's bed just in time. He went into Mam's bedroom and closed the door with a loud rattle – I stood downstairs and waited in our passage. He was upstairs for hours and hours and I heard Mam crying out, then he came downstairs, and he washed his hands in our wash house sink and I could see the blood running away down the plughole. Then he ruffled my hair and went. And that was it.

Mam, slowly, got better, and she started up her sewing again, but she didn't play the piano for a long time and she never said why she had been poorly.

It was ages later that I found out from our Gwendy, when we were in bed and had switched the light off. Mam had been going to have a baby.

"There must have been something wrong with it, because it came away early, it was premature," said our Gwendy.

I had heard this once on our farm when my dad chucked a premature baby lamb on a fire that he had lit in the corner of our paddock. The baby had been born too soon.

"There must have been something wrong with it," said Dad. "It's a good job it came away early."

The baby lamb could not live, of course, it wasn't properly developed, and it looked more like a red fish than a lamb and it had not got wool on it – just slimy, slippery, red skin. You could see its heart beating, though. Anyway, Dad just chucked it on his fire in the corner, it burnt with a hissing and a spitting and it changed to a black brittle hollow blob. When I poked it with a stick it fell apart and turned to a grey ash like a dead leaf. Thick smoke went in the air and I could smell it then. It was a thick deadly smell. It was a frightening body burning smell.

"What did Doctor Moon do with the baby? He didn't chuck it on the fire, did he?"

"No, he flushed it down the lavvy."

"Toilet – Mam said we have to say 'toilet'," I whispered.

Then I thought of that little baby like a tiny red fish – I wondered if it swam and if its heart was still beating when it was flushed away.

"Was it a girl or a boy?"

"It was a boy... I think, well it could have been a boy," said our Gwendy. That baby boy had gone down our toilet into our drain and then into the River Humber where it would be flushed into the North Sea.

And now I can hear Mam playing the piano again, I know that tune! She has played it before a long time ago. It's '*The Elizabethan Serenade*', a sad tune, but now we can get back to normal, and things will carry on as they always have.

Mam

Doctor Moon said that it was nature having its last fling. I wish it hadn't, but at least I know what was wrong with me. I felt so poorly; I did not know what to do with myself. You fear the worst, don't you? I tried to get on with things but sitting at my sewing machine was just too much, I felt so weak. I couldn't play the piano either. I felt so sick. In a way, it is a relief now that it is all over.

I did not want to be expecting, and it was a shock when I thought that I might be. Surely not? At my time of life! Whatever would everybody think? But it was true, and my body was changing and protecting that life, and now it has gone, and I don't know where it has disappeared to. It does not seem real that a life has just vanished into thin air. I wonder if it was my fault. How did I lose a baby?

"How are you doing, love?" That was Herb. I knew he was trying to be kind. He wanted me to get better and get over 'it'. And I will, I'll put the kettle on straight away. I did not say anything about how I felt, you just have to get on with it. What's done is done.

But putting the kettle on and having a cup of tea did not really help me, though I tried to smile for Herb's sake. I need to get back to helping with the cows – one of Sid's lads, Terry, is helping with the milking for now, but really, it's my job. And then there's all that sewing piling up in the corner, there's a dress of my sister Peggy's to alter. She would have made a good mother, Peggy, but she always had her career. She married late – too late to have children, I think.

I never told our girls anything about the facts of life – well, they could watch every day on the farm, so I didn't see the need. I didn't like talking about anything like that, it was embarrassing. I wasn't told anything, and I managed.

My children just came along, and I didn't even think about it. It was not up to me to think about that sort of thing. Though, I was glad when all that business of childbearing was over, and I could get more time for my embroidery. At least, I thought it was over, and then all this happened. I hadn't been feeling well and just put it down to my age. Women my age often don't feel well but they get over it as time goes on. They have to get over things if they are running a busy household and helping their husbands, like me.

Even though I haven't finished her dress, I have decided to go and see Peggy. She always makes me feel better and Sunnyside is a tonic for me. I remember when I lived there. I have such wonderful memories with all my brothers and sisters together. I suppose it is with Mother dying early that we have all clung together like we do.

Peggy smiled her huge smile as soon as I walked in and I felt brighter. Henry fussed around me pulling up a chair near the fire and then put the kettle on.

"Doctor Moon said that it was nature having its last fling," I whispered to Peggy when Henry was out of earshot.

"He said that to me, as well."

"Why would he say that to you?" I was puzzled.

"Oh, I had a bit of a 'do' a week ago – nothing like you though, how are you now?"

And so, we spent the afternoon sitting in comfy seats with Henry busying in and out from the garden.

We talked about when we were young and how our father adored our mother and how he tried to give her everything. In the end, he could not give her anything. He was such a gentle trusting man and he went into partnership with a friend. They bought a farm just outside Ringam and that is where we all lived. Seven brothers and sisters with their mother and father. But he was too kind to be a businessman — it was his downfall. Herb always says that in business you must look out for yourself. I have never agreed with that really, but there was nothing I could do to change his mind.

And there was nothing I could do to change Peggy's mind when she said, "We are thinking of selling Sunnyside and moving down south."

"Why would you go so far away?" I blurted out in disbelief. Peggy going south of the Humber. I didn't like to think about it.

Sunnyside was our place of safety after Dad went bankrupt. Our aunties had taken us in and given us a roof over our heads. All nine of us lived there and made it our home until Mother died. It was an impossible situation — we were far too crowded, and we had so little money. But we all stuck together.

Father never worked again even though he was not old enough to retire. We all got jobs as soon as we could, but not him. He was a strong Methodist and he would not work with just anybody. He tried working on a building site, but he said that the lads were too rough and their language too foul, so he gave up. Our good life on the farm had well and truly ended. We all came to Sunnyside and he refused to go out after that, and Mother's beautiful life ended.

"Please don't go away," I urged Peggy.

"Well, maybe not now, but there is nothing to keep us here. It is not as if we had children or a job to keep us. If our baby had lived it might have been different. But as it is, we are wanting more from life and we are prepared to take on any jobs."

She was so matter of fact and really, that's how I am. Life moves on, but I do enjoy seeing Peggy to have a natter.

"We want a bit more from life," she said.

I thought about what she said when I was on the bus home. I know what she means. I would love to see more of life but what could I do? I was tied to the farm and my family and all the jobs. And when I thought about it, I would love to move to a new house. Now that we know we will not have any boys of our own to share the work with Sid's boys, the thought of a little cottage of our own was very exciting. I knew that Herb would not want to do any other job, but he might like a little farm away from here. We could start a new life like Peggy and Henry were thinking about, before it's too late.

Oh, thinking of a new life makes me wonder about that baby that was inside me – we can't be sure, but it could have been a little boy. Herb would have loved that, I could have given him what he has always wanted, at last. I know I said that it was a relief, but I keep thinking that there was a little living thing inside me and now it's gone. Gone where? Was it in all that blood? Was it in the pain? The thoughts went round and round in my head and would not go away.

This is no use, I must get on; as I say, what's done is done. I'll play a favourite tune and then do the alterations to Peggy's dress.

My fingers gently fly over the familiar piano keys and the haunting words of *'The Elizabethan Serenade'*, pour out of my mind – it's about a love so sweet but no longer there.

Chapter 3

Foreign visitors

Me

Things got exciting at Ripsea school when we had to read *Ali Baba and the Forty Thieves*. I loved the cave that opened when you said, 'Open sesame' and I liked it that Ali Baba got all the treasure for himself because he was good, and his brother and the thieves were bad. But I didn't like to think of his brother being chopped up, even though he was a cheat.

I felt like a bit of a cheat at Ripsea, because I had gone into a trial class to see if I was clever enough for the grammar stream, it was a long trial and I was always worried that I was not good enough. I liked our English teacher though; he was very kind and had told us the story of Ali Baba, which I also liked. But we were soon on to our French lesson, which I did not like, because I did not understand.

I didn't understand any French at all, well I wouldn't, would I? I had never heard another language. Nobody spoke French on our farm, we didn't need to, we all spoke plain English. Even this second stranger to come to our door, spoke English, though he looked like a foreigner. He was a seller who came tramping down our lane with a suitcase – mind you he did not speak *plain* English – I suppose that was because he was not English.

It was exciting – two unknown people had been to see us. We hadn't had even one stranger last year and then we had two this year. It was very unusual, and he was very unusual, as well, because he had a big turban on his head and drapes that were red with a silver thread, and come to think of it, the material looked like brocade, just like our Gwendy's dress.

I thought he looked like Ali Baba and there he stood, and there we stood, and we gawped at each other. He went to Aunty

Vera's door and knocked. He didn't even knock on our door, he went straight next door, so we followed him.

"Come in, love," said Aunty Vera as soon as she saw the Ali Baba man, and in he went to sit near the fire in the chair where the gypsy lady had sat. Grandma chewed her cud, which as you know, was not a good sign.

The man sat down, and while Aunty Vera got him a cup of tea and some of her sponge cake with jam and cream, I noticed, for the first time, that he had a shiny suitcase with him. I must have missed it before because it was hidden under his flowing, glowing clothes. He ate his cake with his thin brown fingers, once he had started, he didn't stop, he just kept on eating and eating, till he had finished. Then, with a beaming smile he dabbed his lips with his pure white handkerchief. He drank his tea with his delicate little finger stuck out. Then he wiped his lips again.

He got up slowly, and gently put his suitcase on the table, you just knew by the way he stroked it there was something very important inside, it was locked, and I must say I expected him to say, 'Open sesame,' and, as if by magic, the lid would fly open and inside would be rubies beyond price. But, after fumbling among the shining fabrics round his waist, he found a key tied with silken thread. He fumbled some more, and the lid was prised open. And there was his treasure for all of us to see. His case was not full of jewels, but it was full of beautiful blouses threaded with gold and silver.

"Oo aren't they gorgeous?" gasped Aunty Vera putting her hands out as if to delve into the treasure. But the Ali Baba man was there before her and carefully took out the first blouse. He waved it in the air like a magician's handkerchief that has a dove inside – there was no dove, but the blouse had silken threads with embroidery of twining, trumpet flowers and strange animals that I had never ever seen round here.

"Beautiful blouses, fit for a princess," said the man in a strange foreign accent, "try this one – you will feel like a

24

princess, as well as looking like one." Aunty Vera took the blouse and went into their passage, when she came back, she was wearing the black blouse with shiny trumpet flowers and strange animals. The material looked as if it was made of spiders' webs — the ones you see very early on an autumn morning just after the sun has got up.

"Ooo."

"By gum you look good," said Uncle Sid who had just come in for a mug of tea.

"Smashing."

"But does black suit me?"

I ran to get Mam. "Come and see," I shouted. "Come and see Aunty Vera."

Well, when I got back Uncle Sid had practically bought the whole suitcase full of blouses for his smashing Vera.

"And for the princess?" he said to Mam. The man held up a blouse left at the bottom of the suitcase for Mam to look at. I thought he said that Aunty Vera was the princess, but I didn't say anything, I didn't want to upset anybody.

Mam shyly smiled and put out her hand to feel the soft material.

"Try it on, you will feel like a princess, as well as looking like one."

Mam went into the passage and came back wearing a red blouse, it suited her, what with her having black hair. The trumpet flowers twisted round her bust and the strange animals galloped round her neck and looked up at her face. We all looked up at her face and she smiled nervously.

"I can't afford this," she said trying to smooth the twisted flowers. "Fetch your dad."

I ran off again, as fast as I could, and found Dad feeding our pigs.

"Come quick," I shouted. "Mam wants you." But he didn't rush and took ages finishing pouring water on the mash he had made for his scoffing, smelly pigs.

I ran back ahead of him and, at last, he burst through Aunty Vera's door looking worried.

"What's up?" he said, and I could feel the warm stink of his pigs filling the house and creeping up to the precious suitcase full of treasure.

"What do you think?" asked Mam, pawing the spider material with her hands.

"How much?" Dad was always careful with money — nearly every penny he and Uncle Sid earned went back into the farm to make it bigger and better — which was right, because, after all, the farm was our livelihood. The blouses were ten shillings each. TEN SHILLINGS! That was four times as much as our Gwendy's dress that Mam had made for her beauty queen competition. Aunty Vera gave Uncle Sid a big kiss for buying her the blouses and my Mam was still just standing there saying, "What do you think?" In the end Dad fished in his pocket and slapped a pound note on Aunty Vera's table.

"Have two," he said and rushed off to get on with his work. The man found the one that Aunty Vera had tried, in black, but did not think it suited her, so Mam had her two blouses. Then the Ali Baba man fastened his case and without even an 'abracadabra' just seemed to disappear — none of us noticed because we were all 'ooing' and 'eeing' over the blouses. Mam quickly ran back to our house to get on with her embroidery that she was doing for a competition at Ringam, she wanted to get some more done before she had to help with milking. I could hardly stop being so excited about the man bringing such beautiful gifts from a foreign land.

Unknown to us though, there was another gift from another foreign land that had arrived, and it came as quietly and secretly as the Ali Baba man had left. It came just as we were all getting on with our lives and we didn't notice it to start with.

Our Gwendy was the first to know about it. She didn't feel very well and had to have a day off school, we all thought it was just a bit of a cold, but it went on to the next day and she was still not any better, then it was all week and she was still in bed.

Then I got it and I was in a collapse. One day I was at school trying to understand how to speak French, and the next I was in bed next to our Gwendy, hardly able to even understand English. We were both just moaning all day long, while our temperatures raged. All was quiet outside, except for Mam and Dad clanking backwards and forwards with buckets full of milk from our cows, and the nonstop pulsing of our milking machines. The world might as well have not been there.

Then after about two weeks – abracadabra – our Gwendy was better and went to school, just like that. But she brought back bad and frightening news. Half the school children were poorly and hardly any teachers were there. A mystery disease had crept up and hit us all.

After another week I was allowed to get up and sit near the fire. Then, when Dad switched the wireless on for the news, we heard that Gwendy and me had caught Asian flu. It had come from abroad and spread across Great Britain and thousands were dead – dropping like the flies when we sprayed them with DDT in our cow shed. And it wasn't over yet.

Mam caught the deadly flu and, as I got better, she got worse. Out Katy had to come from Hull to look after her and Doctor Moon was sent for. Mam was in her bed and our best gold bedspread was put on. Mam was crying out, "The bells, the bells," but we couldn't hear any bells, we didn't have any here. Grandma had some bells in their kitchen, but they were for the servants in the olden days and they didn't ring now. Mam's bells were in her head. Doctor Moon couldn't do anything for Mam.

"Get fluids down her," was all he said, and he rushed off to the next patient – I expect he could hardly cope, what with everybody being so poorly. Mam just kept on getting thinner and thinner, and hotter and hotter, and the bells stayed inside her head giving her headaches all the time. Then Dad got it and he was in bed as well. Uncle Sid had to do all the work on the farm and there was nobody else to carry on except Aunty Vera, it was a good job that she had been a land girl in the war, so she knew all about farms. Then our Katy was needed at the overflowing

27

hospital in Hull where she worked, so she had to go back, and Mam had to help Dad as best she could. She rolled out of bed and struggled to get cups of tea. We sat near the fire just waiting for the time to go by.

Doctor Moon came again, but Dad shouted, "Go away! You have just come for your half a crown." Well, of course he hadn't, now we had the national health. But Dad was delirious and didn't know what he was saying, you did not have to pay for the doctor to visit, not like when I was born. Now it was free 'from cradle to grave' Mam said, but she was not properly better yet, and I hoped that she was not thinking about her grave with that saying of hers.

Mam couldn't do the washing and she had to wear her red, then her black foreign blouse, because she hadn't got any more clean clothes. She didn't look so good in them now, because she was so skinny and weak. Red was for blood and black for the grave and I couldn't bear to think about that.

The whispering started again at night with my mam and Uncle Sid, it couldn't have been about the new man in Aunty Vera's life because she had her baby boy now. I listened on the bottom step of our stairs, just behind the door, in my nighty nearly every night, but I could not make out one real word.

"Wsss, wsss, wsss."

Then Uncle Sid and Aunty Vera and all their kids got Asian flu and they were all in bed and nobody was well enough to struggle out to feed the animals and milk the cows. The farm hands, who had got better from flu, had to manage by themselves and I didn't know how they could do it.

For days and days, we sat there, Mam and me near the fire, on our horse hair chairs, with Dad upstairs in bed waiting for the abracadabra day when we might all get better. And then one day it happened for Dad – one day he woke up feeling a bit better and it was not long before he was back to work feeding his animals and milking his cows. Everybody next door seemed to get better about the same time, and it wasn't long before everything was nearly the same again.

I gradually got better, but it was different for Mam. She was weak and thin for ages and ages and her bust had shrunk. At last, I went back to school and I couldn't believe it, because my English teacher had got flu and died, my kind teacher, who had told us about Ali Baba and the forty thieves, was dead. He was dead and in his grave already. He was as dead as the cheating brother in the story – even though my teacher had not tried to steal anything, as far as I knew.

We had a new young teacher now, who was lanky and thin and not at all kind. They put up a photo, in the front entrance of the school, of my dead teacher in a red knitted jumper, so we wouldn't forget him. But we had to get over it all and I suppose we did forget him really – you do, don't you? We got on with our lives and with our new, thin lanky teacher – and it was as if we had always had him to teach us.

Mam didn't wear her foreign blouses ever again. I expect they were too big for her now, after she had lost weight, what with her having the flu so badly. I hoped that she didn't disappear like the blouse seller and our teacher, it was awful to think that she might die and then I would have lost the chance to show her that I was the daughter that was like her.

Mam

I didn't really like those blouses, you know, they were made of thin muslin and the embroidery was machine done, and not ended off properly. I could see all that, after I brought them back to our house, though I got carried away at the time.

"They all come from the docks in Hull," my brother Tom told me. "It's cheap stuff shipped here for salesmen, to cart round the houses." I suppose they did a good trade, what with us all being so starved of nice things in the war, well I know I was. The blouses were not good quality but when Herb put a pound note down on the table, I couldn't resist.

"You never buy me clothes," I said to him, in shock at him giving me some money for the blouses.

I didn't want to seem ungrateful, but I wished Herb had given me £1 to spend in Hull on a dress. Oh, I would have loved that, walking round the shops with a pound note in my purse. It would have been as if I was in heaven, I could have bought a permanently pleated skirt. I'd seen them there in Hull, made from Terylene, they said that it was a miracle fibre, but I had never had any. 'Easy to wash, no need to iron and the permanent pleats never fall out,' they said. That was what I really wanted. But I never got enough money for clothes – just housekeeping. I saved what I could, but of course, I was only able to save enough to buy cheap scraps of material and then make my own clothes and I couldn't make the permanent pleats.

I could do my embroidery though, and I didn't mean that quick stuff of improbable animals and plants on those cheap blouses, from Hull docks.

I tried to keep an hour in the early afternoon to work on my pieces. I cooked dinner for Herb then, while he had a sleep, I did the washing up. I gave him a cup of tea at one o'clock, then I got changed into clean clothes and took my little embroidery case out and carried on with my stiches.

Sometimes before tea, if I hadn't any clothes to make, I had a bit longer to spare in the afternoons so I could do more embroidery before the light went. The electric light was good but there was only one in the centre and it was a low wattage, so it didn't cost much. Daylight was better.

I was working for a competition, embroidering flowers that I saw in my sister Martha's garden. Pansies were my favourite and I tried hard to get the texture of their soft velvet petals. I was working on pale cream silk, so I had to be very careful not to leave it out, even for a minute, or it would get marked and spoilt. I kept it in my little grey case. I had saved my housekeeping a shilling at a time and then went to Hull and bought it. It was only cheap, but it was clean and safe, and I liked it better than the showy garish case of that salesman.

My embroidery tucked away safe inside, was better to me than any hoard of foreign blouses. I was so happy when I was doing that embroidery; it was mine, and it was clean and as good as it could be.

When the Asian flu arrived though, I had to stop my embroidery altogether – everything stopped, in fact the whole country seemed to come to a standstill, with all the families that I knew being affected.

I didn't know how we could keep going, first one of us poorly and then the other. We had eggs and milk and hams that I had salted, but there were other things I needed like washing soap and disinfectant.

"How's tricks?" asked Sid when he came in one morning.

"Not good," I whispered to him about it, I did not want the girls upset. But I didn't know how we could keep on coping.

"What are we going to do?"

"We'll manage, you'll see," said Sid.

Then Herb got it and I was in despair.

We had to rely on Vera and Sid to go shopping. They normally worked on the land together. They were in charge of arable and Herb and me were in charge of the animals.

"We're just off to Ringam," shouted Vera.

"Do you want any shopping, love?" I didn't like having to ask Vera for anything, I liked to stand on my own two feet, but I had no choice.

"I'll give your house a bit of a scrub, if you want," shouted Vera again the next day. "No need to be proud."

"No thanks, I can manage," my words came out a bit too sharply. I wanted to be independent, but the truth was I couldn't manage, and the house grew filthy. Our Katy did her best to clean but she soon had to go back nursing, as so many people were poorly, and she was needed urgently at the hospital in Hull. We were all like wet rags for weeks and so were our clothes. I hardly had the strength to wash. Our wash house was cold and damp, and I was so weak I could not even carry my basket to the washing line in the orchard. I had to put everything round the fire on our clothes horse. Our room got damp as well. It wasn't healthy, and I was glad when the girls could get out of the house and get back to school. Then, after two weeks Herb was back on his feet, he got better faster than me. He was up and off to his cows and pigs and sheep.

Strangely, Grandma didn't get the flu, even though she was old, and you would have thought that she would be vulnerable. I was sitting with Vera and Grandma next door one day. I used to go every morning for a bit of a chat and to read the newspaper.

"I've seen it all before," she said. "We had Spanish flu in 1918, now that really was flu, killed thousands."

"You're very strong aren't you, Grandma?" said Vera smiling.

"We knew how to deal with flu in them days. I hired a nurse for our Herb."

"She aired Herb's sheets by sleeping on them for one night, didn't she, Grandma?" We'd heard it all before. Grandma didn't answer.

"Then she put them on Herb's bed, so you were sure they were dry weren't you, Grandma?" asked Vera, though she knew the story as well as we all did. We had heard it all that many times.

When Vera and Sid and their kids got the flu, Grandma said dolefully, "You should have hired a nurse." Poor Grandma.

"No need," grinned Vera. "We'll be better before you know it." And it was true. They soon bounced back up and ready for work within the week. Maybe it was because they were younger than us.

I have been talking to Sid again about us moving on and getting another place. Now it is final that I will not have a baby boy. We got into an argument and had to whisper, and sharp words were said.

To cheer myself up, I have bought some of the new Premium Bonds from the Post Office today. I am sure it will be my turn to be lucky soon. I certainly need something to boost my spirits after the flu.

It was my turn to be lucky sooner than I thought — I have won the embroidery competition at Ringam. It was only a Women's Institute effort, but I feel so pleased and it has given me courage to try further afield.

In the Bus Queue
The author (age 11)

Chapter 4

Staying put

Me

Once, when I was in primary school, I remember Dad coming in our car to pick us all up from Ringam school. It was exciting because we never went back home in our car, we always had to get the bus to Gum, where we lived. Well, that time it was different, and my friend Brenda came running to tell me that our car was waiting for us at the school stiles. I went rushing round to tell our Gwendy and then Terry and Stewy, my cousins from next door. It was good fun, I remember. Then, when we were all trying to crowd in, Dad said, "Hurry up we're moving."

Well, I thought, that is even more exciting, we are moving to another house.

"Where are we going?"

"Home, where do you think?"

"You said we were moving."

"You daft beggar, I meant the car was moving, the hand brake isn't working very well."

"Oh."

So we weren't moving to a new house after all, and Dad had only come to pick us up because he had been to the grain merchant in Ringam and was going past our school. It wasn't exciting at all, as it turned out.

But then last night, I thought that something must be about to happen because the whispering was going on again – with Mam and Uncle Sid in our passage. It was stronger and sharper, and I could nearly, but not quite, make out any words.

"Wsss, wsss, wsssss."

They went on for ages and ages, and so in the end I got fed up and crept back into bed from the bottom of the stairs, which was my listening post. I thought something was surely going to happen in the morning, but when I woke up everything was the same and I went off to school as usual.

I'm thinking about moving now, and that if we did move to another house I could go to another school and not dread French lessons, which I do, because they are awful for me. I wanted to do well because Mam was good at English and she would have been good at French if she had the chance, I'm sure. But she hadn't the chance, so it was up to me.

The Deputy Head took us for French; she was an old lady who had been a prisoner in the war that ended on the day that I was born. She was the one that told us about the girls' special toilet and I still didn't really understand what it was for.

She always wore knitted outfits, and her face was so full of wobbly lines, it looked as if her skin had been knitted as well. She hobbled into our French room carrying a case. It wasn't like the case that held the blouses because it was hard and black and square. You just knew that there was nothing nice inside.

'There will be nothing nice inside that case,' I thought, as I sat in silence with my arms folded like she had told us to do.

"Bonjour, la class," she said. Well, I didn't know what she was taking about, so I didn't say anything, but some other kids answered in French while I folded my arms even tighter and hugged myself in.

"Bonjour, la class," she said again but louder.

Again, I didn't answer

She frowned at me and went out again and came back in again and said the same thing. I did the same thing and still I didn't answer. I knew she could speak English because she had told me off once, in perfect English, so I couldn't see the point of what she was doing. Her words were as bad as the whispering at night with Mam and Uncle Sid and I was none the wiser, even after listening really hard.

Anyway, our French teacher who called herself 'Mademoiselle', got really mad with me, but I couldn't do anything to get her out of her anger. I didn't understand what she was saying, and she would not speak plain English. This was getting us nowhere, so I tried a smile but that didn't work, Mademoiselle only scowled back at me and stood over me and wouldn't budge.

"BONJOUR," she said in my ear.

Some of her spit landed on my cheek, but I daren't wipe it off. So, it just sat there in a blob on my face.

"Bo...on...jur?" I whispered wrapping my arms even tighter round myself and speaking to the floor.

"Ah en marche," she walked away, at last, and I breathed out and wiped my cheek as she went towards her black square case.

'Click' went the catches.

It was open and the lid hinged back. I was right, it didn't hold anything nice like Mam's embroidery and it did not have the magic blouses in. It was a gramophone player and she put a record on the peg in the middle and then put a handle in the side and wound it up. Then she carefully put the needle on, and songs came out, in what I thought must be French. Mademoiselle smiled and swayed to the rhythm, but I couldn't tell what any of the words were saying because I couldn't understand French. The words were all scratchy and blurred, as if somebody had half rubbed them out. I wished that I could have been rubbed out then, and not be in that class where there was no plain English at all. I wished that when I had been rubbed out, I could be drawn in again in another school where I would do better. But we weren't going to move, and I had to stay at the same old school, doing the same old boring French.

But then I found out that something that was not boring was about to happen. Our Katy was going to get married. Things were exciting, all of a sudden, and I could forget school and French for now.

She got married to a very nice man at Gum church in cold February. Dad said it was a good idea to get married before the end of the tax year in April, so that's what she did. I was not a bridesmaid, but our Gwendy was, and Mam made her a lovely shiny satin dress. It was a freezing day, but we all had a good time at the village hall afterwards and we put the paraffin stoves on, to warm ourselves up. They went to live in Hull and that was the end of our Katy coming home on her days off.

Mam only had two of us at home now, and I still hadn't been able to be like her. Then I hit on a good idea, she loved embroidery and she was very good at it, so I reckoned that I should try that.

If I could do embroidery, I would be more like her. I asked Mam, if she could set me up with a piece of her linen. She cut off a piece and then she gave me a few strands of embroidery thread. But what to do next was a mystery, almost as puzzling as French lessons. I got Mam's embroidery book, called *Dictionary of Embroidery Stitches*, out of her grey case. I put a knot in the thread and set about choosing a stitch to learn. It was my embroidery book now really, but Mam used it and it was in her case because it used to belong to her.

You see, because I was trying to be like her, I thought I needed an embroidery book with stitches in to learn.

So, when it was my birthday Mam said, "What do you want for your birthday?" Well, I knew straight away what I wanted – I wanted Mam's embroidery book. That was something very special to her and she always kept it safe in her grey case. If she gave me the book, I could get going on some embroidery and learn to be like her.

"I would like your embroidery book ...please."

"What do you mean?"

"I would like your embroidery book for my birthday."

"I can't afford a new one."

"No, I meant the one you keep in your grey case."

"But that's mine, I need it."

"Yes, but that's what I would like for my birthday – your embroidery book."

"Well, alright then you can have it, but I need it in my grey case because I use it every day."

"But it is mine really?"

"Alright then."

And that was that. My birthday present was kept in Mam's grey case and she used it every day, so it didn't really seem mine. When it was the day of my birthday, I asked Mam if I could have my book just for that one day and she agreed and gave it to me. I opened the book and on the first page, which was blank, I wrote my name.

After that, the embroidery book went back in Mam's case again and everything was the same as it always had been, except that it had my name in.

Now, I had to get on with turning the pages and looking at the stitches. There were masses of stitches all in alphabetical order going from 'A', Algerian stitch (plaited) to 'Z', zigzag stitch. It was all such a puzzle, but I did like the little drawings I saw there. Basket-filling stitch had a black woman taking her washing from the line and filling her basket with it. Coral stitch had a man with no clothes on, under water chopping down a tree growing on the seabed, but all that was getting me away from what I was supposed to be doing. In the end I chose a stitch, any old stitch just to get started.

It is cross stitch. I stitch carefully all-round the edge in blue which is Mam's favourite colour. I will be good at embroidery like Mam.

You can make things happen if you try hard enough, like Mam thinks that she will win at Premium Bonds by looking for her numbers in the *Hull Daily Mail* every month. She was so excited I could see the paper trembling in her hands.

Mam

It was so hard to believe that our Katy was old enough to get married, it did not seem two minutes since I got married myself.

When Herb proposed to me everybody was envious. A house, a farm and an income, what more could I want? Girls didn't have much of a choice in my day. There weren't many young men or women to choose from in these parts. Not many new young people came to live here. So, you had to choose from what was here.

I remember Herb telling me that if young men came into Ringam, say for a dance, the resident locals threw stones at them to keep them away – the local lads had to have first choice of their own women. I was luckier than some I could mention who stayed single or married into a struggling family. And thank goodness, my girls could go out into the world and choose the life they wanted and who they wanted to marry.

I know it is selfish of me, but now I dream about moving away from here. I whispered to Sid about it again but there was nothing to be done. So, I snatched an hour or so in the afternoon to get on with my embroidery.

I did not know why our Vi wanted my embroidery book. My embroidery was the only thing I had for myself, it made no difference – my book was still in my case. I supposed she could have it when I was dead and gone.

But I wasn't dead and gone yet and I would not let the subject of moving drop altogether. I did for a time, because I had our Katy's wedding to think about. She made her own dress, but I had our Gwendy's bridesmaid dress to make. Everything had to be just right, there was no going to the remnant shop this time for our Katy. I had to meet her in Hull, and we went round the posh shops so that we could get good material. I didn't blame her wanting good things.

The material was very heavy and shiny, and I did not get on very quickly with our Gwendy's dress. But it looked fine when it was finished, in fact everything looked good on her; she had a lovely figure and she looked so graceful. Not like Vi who was always thinking seriously about things and not having time to smile. She was struggling with her embroidery as well – I could not work out why she wanted to do it.

Because I had taken so long with our Gwendy's dress, I decided not to make my own outfit or Vi's suit and I managed to persuade Herb to pay. It was a first for me – not making all our clothes and it felt strange buying clothes. But why not? We needed warm coats in 'tax rebate February' – like our own wedding which had to be at a quiet time on the farm – 'nithering November'. Everything revolved round money and the farm.

Katy made a lovely bride, and she had a beautiful fur trimmed coat for her honeymoon on the North Sea Ferry. I can see her now in my imagination – so smart and proud. I couldn't help but smile.

"What's that smell?" I was suddenly jerked out of my thoughts by Herb.

"What do you mean?" I had been daydreaming and had just put Herb's breakfast of bacon and eggs on the cooker. "What smell?"

He rushed down our passage shouting. I turned round, to see a black smoking mess in the frying pan.

"What are you doing?"

"I was cooking your breakfast."

"Well I can't eat that, can I?"

"No, I'd better start again." I cleaned out the black pan and put fresh eggs and bacon in. What was I thinking of? This time I did not take my eyes off the pan until everything was ready. I dished up and carried the plates to our table in our room. Herb was late for feeding the animals and it was my fault for burning the breakfast. No wonder he wasn't pleased all day. I escaped to Sunnyside again in the afternoon for an hour.

"I've put Sunnyside up for sale," Peggy told me as soon as I walked in. "Henry has got a house with a job in Southampton. He's helping children with problems."

"What sort of problems?"

"Anything, he'll help. It's like a hospital really, but he's just there to get them doing little jobs."

I stare around – she has already started clearing out. Henry was burning stuff on a big bonfire in the garden. Everything went on it – even family photos with people standing near chairs with aspidistra plants on a table.

"Nobody knows who they are. It's no good us taking them all that way."

The flames burst from the fire and smoke got into the house and hurt my eyes.

"I'd better shut that window that smell will linger."

But I cannot smell anything.

On the bus home I think of our family house, Sunnyside, and how we had all lived there at one time with the aunties. How many comings and goings there had been through that gate onto Green Lane. Sunnyside was such a safe haven to us all, even though it was so crowded when we were taken in, when things were difficult.

As soon as I get home, I can see that there is a letter for me, it's postmark is St Annes. It was from ERNIE – I have won on the Premium Bonds. I have won £5.

"You're lucky with things like that," said Herb. And it is true, I am lucky in competitions.

Chapter 5

New horizons

Me

I am embroidering a bunch of flowers. Mam had got a picture that came free with her old-fashioned women's magazine. The picture was drawn in purple and when she ironed it, with a cool iron, the flowers were printed on my linen.

"When I was at work, doing embroidery, we were not allowed to use a transfer like this."

"How did you know where to do your embroidery stitches then?"

"We traced the design drawn onto tissue paper and we put that on the material, then put fine pins through it as markers."

"I can't see what's wrong with this transfer," I said, looking at the pale purple bouquet, I was already thinking about which stitches I could use. Maybe I could copy the coral stitch from Mam's book (which was now my book, but still in her grey embroidery case) or the zigzag stitch which looked easy.

"It would be a disaster if any of the purple showed, so it was banned. Nowadays there is a yellow transfer which hardly shows, but it would have been harder for you to follow," said Mam.

I set to work. I enjoyed choosing the colours from Mam's collection of embroidery threads – she had hundreds – but I hadn't been stitching long before I started to make mistakes. The new stitches were harder than I thought and soon my threads were knotting up and getting in the wrong place. Then there were sweaty fingers, which made grey stains on the cloth. I am wondering about giving up embroidery.

Mam never gave up with her embroidery though, even when Uncle Teddy and Aunty Gladys came to see us. Uncle

Teddy was her brother and she loved to see him, she didn't get to see him very much because he lived down south now. He had dark hair like Mam, and he was really good looking.

"He is a country person at heart," said Mam. "He worked on our farm when he was young." Well, I could tell he loved farming because as soon as he got here, he had a chat with his sister, who was Mam, then he went out to work on our farm.

They were supposed to be on holiday, but it was the same with Aunty Gladys. As soon as she had drunk her cup of tea, she put one of Mam's pinnies on and started sweeping the floor. They worked all the time and I played with my little cousins. There was Rosemary, Heather and Bryony. Rosemary and Bryony had blonde hair and Heather had dark hair and they were all so pretty.

"My little posy," Aunty Gladys called them. We played with my dolls and then we made a den in our bales.

"Time to go," that was Mam shouting us, I could see her standing in her pinny in our stack yard, but she couldn't see us because we were in our den.

"We are here," shouted Bryony scrambling out and running up to Mam in excitement.

"It's time to catch the bus," said Mam.

"But I don't want to go," wailed Bryony, while we all just stood and stared.

"You are going back to Sunnyside."

"Yes, and this is our last holiday there," said Aunty Gladys. "So we had better make the most of it, and we are all going shopping in Hull tomorrow. We need to get to bed and get plenty of rest, ready for our big day."

I went with them up to our lane end, where we all stood on the little bare patch of mud and looked out for the bus coming over the horizon from Sunkstead.

It didn't seem like two minutes before Mam and me were walking back up our lane and waiting for the bus coming in the other direction. You had to be there at the end of our lane and watch carefully, because this time the trees in our wood were in the way, and the bus was on you before you had time to blink.

When we got on the bus, Bryony ran up to me and dragged me to a seat with her. Mam sat with Aunty Gladys and they talked all the way there. We got off at Paragon station in Hull and worked our way down the shopping streets. They went in every clothes shop they could find. I was fed up. We went to a café called Gainsborough, for fish and chips, and then they set off again to Whitefrigate, where they said all the good shops were.

"This is such an exciting place, and to think it was nearly all bombed in the war," said Aunty Gladys, striding out past our Willis Ludlow store, and still heading eagerly for Whitefrigate.

"What's this old building?" I pointed.

"It's Ferens Art Gallery," said Aunty Gladys. "I'm surprised that you didn't know."

Why would I know? Nobody had told me about it. I stared at the massive carved pillars in front, then I could see that it said 'Ferens Art Gallery' in big gold letters above the pillars.

"Can we go in?"

"No, what do you want to go in there for? We are going shopping," said Mam.

"I don't want to come with you, shopping is boring."

"Shopping is boring," copied Bryony pulling a funny face.

In the end, it was agreed that I could go in, and they would come back in an hour and collect me. I would wait at the door and we would go to Paragon station, in time for the bus home.

"Your grandmas' cousin has a painting in there," Aunty Gladys shouted after me.

"Which grandma?" I shouted back, but they were gone, and out of hearing, rushing towards the shops, with three little girls in tow.

I went up the stone steps, through the pillars with leaves carved on the top, and under the gold letters. I was so excited I had never been in an art gallery before.

It would surely be like going into another world, like Ali Baba's cave, full of riches. I could hardly believe that I was allowed to go in without paying. The entrance was white stone with more pillars going up to the ceiling. Inside was a fountain climbing up to a wrought iron balcony going all round the room. I stood and stared, and it was ages before I went to see the paintings.

The room I chose was brown and dark. I stood puzzled at the big fancy gold framing surrounding paintings of women with bare bosoms and men fully dressed in armour and holding swords. I saw Jesus on the cross and the Virgin Mary with her baby. I saw cherubs and angels coming from the sky. The light wasn't very good, and I had to stand very near to see what was painted there. I looked into their eyes. Big sad eyes looked back at me.

'Who are you?' I asked in my head, but they only stared back sadly with tears on their cheeks.

I could see cracks, like crazy paving, going all over the people and scenery. Why would anybody want to look at these?

I was disappointed. Were these paintings good? They must be, to be in the great Ferens Art Gallery. But I didn't like them much and wondered again why they would have been chosen. They must have been chosen in the olden days by old fashioned people.

Then, as I walked through room after room, all with the same kind of paintings, I suddenly saw one showing a barn. It could have been ours. And there was Dad with his cap on, and his sleeves rolled up, he was carrying a sack on his neck and shoulder. I had seen him do that hundreds of times, with the sack balancing, so he didn't have to use his hands. And then, at the back of the barn I saw some weighing scales just like ours. They were wooden and metal and you put the sack on one side and the big heavy weights on the other until it balanced. My dad did that.

It said, 'Weighing the sacks' underneath and then it said, 'The tithe barn'. My primary school was on 'Tithe Barn Lane', so I liked that. I knew that long-ago farmers had to give a tenth of their corn to the church and it was kept in the tithe barns, but we don't do that now.

The barn had whitewashed walls like ours, and the painter had painted bone-white beams like our skeleton holding us all together.

I felt myself sitting on one of the sacks watching my dad, I could smell the dust in the air and taste the dry husks of the corn.

"Come on, an hour has gone, and we are all waiting for you." That was Mam.

"You haven't obeyed the rule we agreed. You should have been at the door."

I went with her, and it was only when I was rushing to Paragon station that I remembered I hadn't looked for a painting by my grandmas' cousin.

I liked that last painting though, and I thought that I would like to see more new things.

"Can I come back with you?" that was me asking Aunty Gladys if I could go back to their house with them. I had said it before I thought about it. I was excited about my visit to the art gallery and I think that's why I asked. What else was there that I didn't know about? We just did the same old things – I was nice and safe but there must be more, surely. Did that mean I wanted to go away? I wasn't sure.

"We'll have to ask your mam," said Aunty Gladys. "But it is fine by me, you will be very welcome."

And so, before I knew it, everything was arranged, and it was too late to change my mind. I packed a change of clothes in Mam's grey embroidery case and we were off. A friend from Ringam was driving his car down to Wales for a holiday, and he would drop us all off on the way.

Seven of us were squashed up in the car. Five of us were on the back seat. I had Bryony on my knee and Aunty Gladys had Heather or Rosemary, they took it in turns. Sometimes one or two girls sat down at our feet. Uncle Teddy sat in the front because he could map read and so help give directions from his atlas.

"We'll go through the Peak District," said Uncle Teddy. "It's a bit out of our way, but I want you to see beautiful countryside."

I always thought that the countryside on our farm was lovely, but soon I was staring out of the window in disbelief. There were hills that looked blue and trees that looked so green. Ours at home were green but you couldn't see so many at once – ours were on flat land and these were on hills. I could see miles and miles of them.

"Why is that purple?" I asked pointing at the hillside as we wound round on little roads.

"That's heather, isn't it beautiful? We named Heather here after this plant," that was Aunty Gladys and she nudged Heather in the ribs and they both giggled.

We were dropped off outside their semi-detached house, on a new housing estate. It was all very neat and tidy with a three-piece matching suite made out of a sort of plastic. It stuck to my legs when I stood up after I'd been sitting on it. I saw that every chair in the room was pointing to the television. All the rooms were little, compared to ours at home, but everything you needed was there (except, of course, our farm).

Aunty Gladys went to get changed then rolled up her sleeves and began to cook the meal. After that she washed up and dusted round the house. The three girls were packed off to bed after supper, and I was allowed to stay up. I watched their television for hours and they had adverts and I loved them. We didn't have the right aerial at home, so we only had BBC. I waited for the next advert and loved it even more. I longed for the adverts. There was singing and dancing and fun in those advertisements and I soon learnt to sing along with them. I loved the one about toothpaste.

"I'll wonder where the gleam came from..." I copied. "I'll wonder where the clean came from..."

I went to bed in the girls' bedroom. I had a little put-you-up. It was comfy but I couldn't sleep because, all at once, I wanted to go home. What was I doing here? The pain in my gut grew and grew and I longed for my own bed with Gwendy next to me in her bed. But this is what I wanted wasn't it? Yes, I wanted to find out about life somewhere else, well I think I did. I fell into an exhausted sleep with the noise of the telly blaring out its adverts.

A man sang, 'Brings you smiles, over the miles...'

Aunty Gladys and Uncle Teddy arranged all sorts of things for me to do. We went everywhere on the bus. There were a lot of buses here, going to all sorts of places. First, we went to Coventry, which wasn't too far away, and Uncle Teddy pointed out the old bombed cathedral with the brave steeple still standing and the new, modern walls growing alongside. Coventry had been bombed nearly as much as Hull in the war, and just after the war the statue of Lady Godiva was put up. We went to see her – a bare lady riding a horse.

"She was objecting to her husband putting up taxes," said Uncle Teddy and I liked her for that, but I wished that she had kept her clothes on.

Uncle Teddy took me on a bus to see the coal mine, where he worked. I stood and looked at the big black wheel and all the black machinery.

"Do you want to go down the mine?" asked Uncle Teddy, he put his kind arm round me.

"No, no I don't," but I wished now that I had. I would have been safe with Uncle Teddy.

Soon, the man came to pick me up to go home in his car. The pain in my gut had never quite gone, but I had seen so much and learnt so much that I didn't mind too much. We went home a much quicker way than we had gone and soon I was dropped off at our lane end. I carried Mam's little grey case home and sat down with them all and had my tea. Nobody had time to ask me anything because the cows needed milking. It was then, as I sat down near our fire, I realised that embroidery didn't work for me; I am not like Mam in that way. I am giving it up for good – I have my own adventures to think about.

Mam

I really enjoyed seeing Teddy and Gladys with their lovely little children. There is nothing like family. I don't see them often enough, but the journey is hard because they live down south. Every place beyond the Humber is 'down south' to me, and so far away.

Teddy loves working on our farm, as soon as he arrives, he gets changed and goes out to help Herb. He worked for us here, when he was a young lad. He left school and hadn't got a job.

"Can Teddy come here to work?" I begged Herb. "He will be a hard worker and he's no trouble at all."

Then the war started, and we were short of workers because the men were needed for fighting. Teddy was too young to go to war so, in the end, he came here to work. I was pleased because I could keep an eye on my little brother. He stayed at Grandma's, as she had more room than us, but I could tell that she did not like him there. I had baby Katy and evacuees from Hull, so we were full up. Grandma's house had lots of space, especially after all the dreadful things that had happened.

Teddy was always hungry – well he would be – he was a growing lad, wasn't he? Grandma was not keen on him having more food. She always shared it equally. I didn't want to upset Grandma, but I could not let Teddy go hungry, so I made him sandwiches secretly, whenever I had spare bread. Food like bread was short in the war, but I suppose we were luckier than most being on a farm, with our own dairy and meat and vegetables.

Teddy went off down south as soon as he could get another job on a farm, and then he got married to Gladys. They were short of food down there, as well, because when they came to see us, they brought an empty suitcase and they asked if I would fill it with potatoes. We grew potatoes on our land, so we had plenty. He must have been very strong to carry that case – it was like a ton weight. I had made sure it was crammed full so that they would not go short for weeks – I did not think about the weight.

I don't know why Vi wanted to go into Ferens Art Gallery – what would she do in a place like that? She was a nuisance not being at the door when we came back from shopping. After searching for ages, I found her looking at a painting of a barn. I had a look as well, and I could see the roof held up by woodwork that looked like the branches of a tree. As we went back to Paragon station, having to rush because of Vi, I began to think of how that painting reminded me of my new embroidery work.

"That doesn't look like embroidery to me," said Vi, "it looks like a lot of holes."

"It's called drawn-thread work, you have to count the threads and then cut." In fact, it was very hard, concentrated work. I had to stitch round all the holes I made and strengthen all the threads that were left. I had so much to learn and had to buy a new book from my teacher at Ringam. I keep it away from Vi, I do not want her writing her name in that as well. I hug it to myself.

"Did you find the painting by your grandmas' cousin?"

"Which grandma?"

"Both.

"How can that be?"

"Your Dad and I are related, the artist, was a cousin to both." I didn't add that a lot of cousins, and half cousins, married round here because, like in most villages, people stayed in the area and married locally. There weren't always a lot of suitable partners to choose from.

"Did you ask about his picture?"

"No, I didn't know what to ask."

At our next embroidery class Peggy sat next to me.

"Guess what we found in the attic."

"What?"

"Well, after Teddy and his family left, I got going again on the clearing up and thought the attic could do with more sorting. And there, painted on a piece of cardboard, was a picture of Sunnyside."

"Was it painted by our artist?"

"Yes, it was! I suppose he did it one day when he was visiting our aunts. He signed it as well."

"What a find."

"I'll get it framed and it will be a lovely reminder of Sunnyside, when we are down south," said Peggy.

I did not answer because I thought that I had better stop talking and get on with my embroidery. I am working for a competition in Hull that my teacher had pointed out.

"You have a good chance for this competition. Have a go, you have nothing to lose."

She was right, I loved doing the embroidery and I loved competitions and even better, it was for drawn thread work. I started it that night in class at Ringam.

I kept thinking of the picture that Vi was staring at – those strands of wood holding the whole structure together. Each beam depended on the other and made a regular pattern. I was embroidering a tree and I thought I would show the pattern of the branches, and how they all relate to each other. I love the trees in winter and the dark trunks and twigs standing out against the sky. They were ideal for my new drawn-thread work. I became so absorbed in what I was doing, I nearly missed the last bus home.

"Can you imagine ringing Herb for a lift, at this time of night?" laughed Peggy. "He wouldn't want to come all this way."

"Yes," I giggled. "And I don't know where I would find a telephone. I would probably have to go to the police station!"

It was true, I did not know anybody with a telephone except Grandma. There was a phone box, but I had no money on me. I had a return ticket for the bus and that was that. I could do a reverse charge call, but can you imagine the fuss?

I wonder why Vi wanted to go all that way to stay with Teddy, Gladys and the girls. It's up to her, but she is still a puzzle to me.

I spent hours on that drawn-thread work. I was snipping and counting threads in my dreams. I was very pleased with the results though, the lines from branch to branch, and twig to twig showed the pattern, in triangles and squares, which made up its skeleton. To finish off, I stitched a border round it — little white flowers, almost invisible on the cream linen. They reminded me of the flower pattern on the tiles at Madame Clapham's.

I packed it carefully and sent it off. It was open to all East Yorkshire, so I wasn't that confident when I handed it in at Ringam Post Office.

A few weeks later Posty brought me a letter. It was the results of my competition with the Hull postmark — it could not be anything else.

I was Highly Commended; the judges wrote how beautifully I had done the work.

'But,' they added, 'we could not give it first prize because your flower border was done in daisy stitch and not in the required drawn-thread work.' Oh drat! I did not think about that when I embroidered the little flowers. I was rushing and full of excitement about my trees. I had not obeyed the rules.

The winners, including mine, were going on display for a week, in Hull library to promote local crafts. I wish I could go and see it, but it will be hard to find the time.

Sunnyside
Harry Watson (1871-1936) R.W.S., R.W.A., R.O.I.
In private ownership

Chapter 6

Playing with fire

Me

Mam used to stand really near our coal fire to get warm. As soon as she came in from milking that's where she went – near the fire. She stood with her back to the grate warming her bottom. Sometimes she lifted her skirt and warmed the back of her legs.

"You must have thin blood," we laughed, "and that's why you are always so cold."

Then one day Mam caught fire. I mean really caught fire. The ribbon of her pinny must have trailed into the coals.

The smell of the smoke came first. One minute she was standing near the fire, with the yellow flames shooting up our chimney, and the next minute the flames had jumped out of the fire and up onto her pinny and up her bust to her neck – higher and higher the flames went until they were nearly licking her face. Me and Katy were there, and we just stood and stared and stared as if the flames, that were climbing up her, were holding her there and keeping us away. And Mam just stood, shouting, 'Oh drat, oh' in a loud voice and it was as if she was going to be eaten by the flames and never be seen again.

Then I came to life and ran off to our wash house and ran back with a jug of water – it would not be enough, but I didn't know what else to do. Luckily our Katy did know what to do when she suddenly sprang to life. She pushed our burning mam to the floor and onto our clipped rug, near the fire, then she rolled her in it. Over and over she went with Mam just saying, "Oh, oh."

Rolling her in our rug seemed the wrong thing to do, but it turned out to be the right thing to do, because when we unrolled our mam, the hungry flames were dead and had changed from yellow to black and had gone. We were shocked and shaking but after a cup of tea we all felt better, and Mam didn't even have a burn mark on her. Katy had done very well.

And I was doing a bit better at school now and starting to get higher marks.

"You are a late developer," said Mam. "I have heard of this before, you were not ready when you were younger. Sometimes children can break into life when nobody expects it."

'Just like those flames,' I thought. It was a good job I had been given another chance at Ripsea Comprehensive School and that they had waited for me to catch on.

I found that I liked doing well. It felt good and it felt even better when they moved me into the prestigious class. I was in the Upper A stream now and it was as if I had passed my scholarship. There was a B and C class as well as D and E streams. The people in E couldn't do well and Mam said that they didn't know 'what was what'.

There was one girl called Joany in the E class and kids in our school used to laugh at her, she had big teeth and old-fashioned clothes on – it looked like she was wearing her mam's clothes, except that she didn't seem to have a real Mam because people said that her sister was her mam. But that didn't make sense to me and I thought that maybe they did not know 'what was what' either. Anyway, Joany was in the E class and you could tell that she didn't care about her schoolwork, when I saw her on the corridor at school, she was always larking about and laughing her big grinning laugh. A lot of lads got round her and they were laughing as well, but not in the same way.

I thought that nothing like that could ever happen to me. Then I met a lad called Ricky and he started talking to me and walking with me in the corridor. It was funny because he always seemed to be going the same way as me, even though he was in a different class and would not have had the same lessons as me. As soon as I walked out of a classroom door he was there zooming up and suddenly walking with me. He sometimes asked to carry my satchel and I let him because it was so heavy, full of all the books I needed for my lessons. Then, it was funny again, because he was on my bus going home and I had never seen him there before. I used to always sit with Brenda, and she used to save me a seat, but Ricky started to jump on the bus just before me and get me a seat next to him. It all happened so quickly, one minute I was sitting with Brenda and next minute, I don't really know how, I was sitting with this Ricky. I was so surprised by Ricky and wondered what Brenda would think. I wondered what he was doing.

Ricky used to save a double seat. When I got on the bus he used to stand up and block the gangway, so I had nowhere else to go, and had to move onto the seat near the window then he sat down, and it was like I was a prisoner. I felt that I had no choice.

"Would you like to go out with me on Saturday?" he suddenly asked one night on the bus. I didn't answer, I was shocked into silence. I just put my head down and stared at my knees.

"Right then – meet you at Ringam cricket ground at seven o'clock."

He got up for me to get off the bus and it went chugging on, leaving me staring down at the ground swaying under my feet. Why hadn't I said 'No'? Now I was stuck with seeing him, I ran down our lane and tried not to think about it all. But I did think about it and he was spoiling my weekend.

When Saturday came, I went to play with my cousin Suzy at Ringam as I often did. I had my tea and then set off for the cricket ground. I was wearing my little cotton green dress that Mam had made for me out of a remnant. I was getting a bit cold and I was thinking that I should have brought a cardi, and that I should not have come.

What was I doing? I should have said, 'No'. It was as if I wasn't thinking properly doing what Ricky said. I had just decided to turn back and go home when suddenly Ricky was there. He came out of nowhere and – abracadabra – he was next to me.

"Let's sit on this bench," he steered me by walking in front of me and guiding me down. I did as he said again, like a rag doll without a choice. He sat in the middle of the seat and squashed me up against the wooden arm rest. I shivered, then all of a sudden, he put both arms round me, he was keeping me warm and that was alright. But then he pulled me towards him in an iron grip, and that was not alright. I was a pretty strong person myself, being used to farm work and all that, but he was stronger than me. I could see that something had taken over him and he had a strange look in his eyes. Then he started kissing me. My eyes were wide open in fright, and I felt myself go tight and stiff. He closed his eyes for some reason. This went on for a bit, with me like a board and him getting carried away. Then he suddenly let go and held me at arm's length and stared right into my eyes. I couldn't help but stare back. It was then that he winked at me and laughed.

We sat there for ages in the cold and it was getting a bit dark, I knew that I had to get away. I knew that I must do something, anything, but what? Would he let me go?

"I have to go, my mam said I have to catch this bus," I lied.

I jumped free and ran and ran until I was at the bus stop gasping for air and trying not to think of what had just happened. And hoping and praying that he wouldn't follow me. I turned and stared down the road, looking for him, with my heart beating and my mouth dry. Then the bus came round the corner from Ripsea and I jumped on and I was safe.

Mam said you had to be careful going out with boys – it was like playing with fire. I asked her what she meant, but I didn't tell her about Ricky and what he had done.

"Well you know," she said.

I didn't.

"You could get in the family way," Mam was frowning, and I knew that it would be the worst thing that could happen to me.

But why would I do anything like that?

"I don't think I would do anything like that," I said.

"You'll soon find out," she answered, "it's best to keep away."

But I hadn't kept away, had I? Does a tongue give you a baby? No, I knew it couldn't but was I playing with fire?

Then I found out that poor old Joany had definitely been playing with fire, and I don't suppose she knew, what with her being in the E class. There was a rumour at school that she was having a baby. She was in the family way. And everybody was wondering who the father was.

The next day Joany was nowhere to be seen at school. The corridors were quiet now she wasn't giggling and laughing showing her pink gums when a group of lads came round her.

"Haven't you heard?" said Brenda — I was sitting next to her on the bus again, now that Ricky had disappeared.

"She's been sent to a Home a long way from here where she'll be looked after till the baby comes."

Maybe she was in Hull, or maybe Scarborough but that was near the sea and great fun, I didn't think that they would send her anywhere that was nice.

"Who's the father?"

"We don't know," whispered Brenda. We would soon all know.

The father turned out to be Ricky (that's what everybody said anyway) and he was in the A class so he would certainly have known 'what was what'. Brenda said that his dad was very well to do, and they lived in a great big house. It was funny, but I didn't know anything about Ricky, except that he had been wanting me to go out with him and wouldn't leave me alone. Anyway, I had no need to worry about him now because his dad suddenly got promotion to a big firm down south and I would never see him again. Thank goodness, I only just realised, with burning fear, that I had been lucky to escape, like Mam in the fire.

Mam

I had certainly gone too close to the flames when I caught fire. I was always cold these days. It wasn't as if we didn't have a good fire – we had lots of coal. Herb picked it up from the railway station yard in our truck. We had a special compartment in the yard where goods trains dropped off our order. They came in huge black shining lumps and we had to use the axe head to break them. The fire was always roaring in our room, but there was no heating anywhere else in the house. I stood with my back to the fire to warm my legs, sometimes I got scorch marks like little round red marks all over my skin. Even that didn't put me off, though I hated anybody seeing them.

My pinny ribbons must have come undone and somehow got into the fire. I saw the smoke, but I didn't smell anything, which is a wonder because burning material certainly has a pungent smell, I knew that. Thank goodness the girls were there to help.

"I hope you have not been anywhere near that Ricky," I said to our Vi when she came down from doing her homework.

"Joany did not know any better, but you do – and now you know what can happen, be careful, I don't want you having to go away."

Vi hung her head and didn't say anything, she had no idea that girl. I sometimes worry about what she could get into.

She is fourteen. I left school at fourteen and went to work. I just cannot imagine little Vi going to work. I hope she isn't messing about with lads. I didn't go out with anybody until I met Herb and I was much older.

When we left school, most of us girls went into service, but I wanted to sew. It was all I ever wanted to do – sewing and embroidery. So, I risked it, and asked a woman called Miss Sanctuary if I could work for her. She had a little shop in town and was well known in these parts. Her shop was just a room in her house, and people came to her for dressmaking and alterations. She always had a smile and a cheerful word, and her round red face was always breaking into a laugh.

"I could do with some help, love, but I can't afford to pay much." I took the job there and then. I managed; I was doing what I loved. I had to bike to Ripsea every day, it was a push but at least it was flat and if the wind was behind me it helped me along. Mind you it would be a head wind going home.

"You're a good little worker," said Miss Sanctuary smiling at me. She always got me a cup of tea when I got there, and we sat together for five minutes talking about the work we were going to do that day. She never charged her customers much, especially if they were not very well off.

"I like your work. You are neat and quick. Have you ever thought of further training? You have a gift you know," she asked me one morning when I had been there about two years.

"I can't afford to give up my job to train. My mother has taught me to sew and embroider from childhood." "Well, I'll teach you more, if I can — you could go far." How far can you go with sewing? I wondered. But I didn't wonder for long. A week or two later Miss Sanctuary told me about a job going in Hull.

"Madame Clapham is advertising," she told me "It's in the Yorkshire Post, look."

"Madame Clapham!"

"I know, I know, she's a long way up from me, but it's worth a try."

"How can I do that sort of work, when I have had no training?"

"You've had training from me for two years and I'll give you a good reference. In any case, I can't afford to pay you much longer. So, you must move on. Give it a go, love, you are the best I have come across."

So, I applied to Madame Clapham's in my very best neat writing. I wrote her a letter — I could do that sort of thing. I loved handwriting at school, and I copied out of books to get it just right. I dipped my pen in the inkwell and, being careful not to make a blot, I worked on my style. I was glad I did because this was an important letter, though I never thought it would come to anything. I posted it in a neatly addressed envelope from Ripsea Post Office.

After a few weeks I had a letter back. It was on the table waiting for me when I got home from work.

"There's a letter for you, Girly. The postmark is Hull – now who is writing to you from Hull I wonder?" I hadn't told Mother about the application. It didn't seem worth it as there would be so many girls wanting such a prestigious job. I never thought it would come to anything. But it did, and I was surprised, because I was asked for interview! I was very nervous and out of my depth.

Miss Sanctuary told me to get off the bus at George Street and then ask. I got Peggy to cut my straight black hair into a fashionable bob. I wore my mother's best dress, it was dark green cotton, she had made it herself – it was a bit old fashioned, but it was the best of a bad job. All my own clothes were worn to a thread and that would not do if I was anywhere near posh people.

Madame Clapham was a Court Dressmaker and I could hardly believe I was being interviewed. None of my family had ever done anything like this before. I had to catch the early bus and I rushed down the road in Ringam at some unearthly hour, squinting at the church clock. I couldn't see what time it said. I had noticed this recently – my sight was not good at a distance. But I never thought to say anything. I managed the best I could.

I jumped on the bus to Hull and got off at George Street. I walked up to a very big building in Kingston Square. It was painted white and had big bay windows – even the basement had bay windows and the ground was dug out and paved so they could get natural light. There were two sets of steps and I walked up the stone steps on the side, thinking that they would be more suitable. I held on to the mahogany handrail, to steady myself, and stood looking at the green glazed tiles to calm my nerves. They had a discrete flower pattern and they reminded me of wild flowers in green fields.

I was shown into a room on the left.

"Good morning."

"Good morning, madam." It wasn't Madame Clapham. I could see her photograph on the wall near me, with her name underneath, even so I thought I'd better be extra polite.

"Do sit down, my dear."

I sat on the upright wooden chair, and folded my legs then unfolded them. I wore grey socks with my little canvas summer shoes. I wish I had worn stockings, but I hadn't any – I could not afford them. She was wearing stockings of course, they were silk, and her hemline was just high enough for me to see her slim ankle and her two-tone Oxfords with little laces.

"Have you brought me a sample of your work, as you were asked?"

I took a remnant of silk from my bag. I had worked on it for ages, using it like a sampler with all different stitches.

"The back must be as neat as the front, you know." I knew and, of course, I had taken care to ensure that both sides were neat. But I felt so nervous with this woman scrutinising my every stitch.

She turned it over to examine how I had ended each thread.

"Now, you come highly recommended by Miss Sanctuary from the small town of Ripsea. I believe she has a little business. Of course, this is an altogether different establishment."

She asked me some more questions and then I had to go and work on a dress with a supervisor. The dress that had been cut out by somebody else.

She looked at my work. It was easy for me. I had been able to sew and embroider for as long as I could remember. But was I good enough? I went back in the room.

To my surprise, there stood Madame Clapham. It took my breath away, here was THE Madame Clapham herself. I knew her straight away by her bearing and by her fine clothes (and the photograph of course). She wore a long, black silk dress with a lace wrap. She stared at me through little glasses. She looked very old.

"Good morning, my dear. I always like to see any prospective employees myself." I sat down again when she sat down.

"Now, for the purposes of my records, can you tell me what your parents do for a living."

"My father is a farmer – an owner farmer." I decided not to tell her about his dodgy partner and their money difficulties.

"And my mother has never had the need to seek employment." I licked my lips.

"Hmm," she was writing and then looking at my embroidery sample. Then she leant forwards with her hands clasped in front of her.

"I have decided to offer you a job for a trial month, in the first instance. I hope that is satisfactory. Start tomorrow after your medical." She briskly called the next girl in.

They took it for granted that I would accept the job – but I wondered if I had aimed too high. Could I do the work, day after day?

Would the other women think I was not as good as they were? I was only young and inexperienced, and I wondered if I was taking too much of a risk. If I wasn't good enough, I could be dismissed without a reference and it would have been very difficult to get another skilled job. But all I had ever wanted to do was sew and embroider. That's what this job was, and I knew that if I worked hard and was willing to learn, it would be a very good job for somebody like me.

It was a dream come true then, but I remember wondering again if I was risking too much and aiming too high. Would I be good enough? I asked myself for the umpteenth time.

Chapter 7

Facing the music

Me

I started to go to Hull for my music lessons. Mrs Treasure, my old piano teacher, said to Mam that she couldn't teach me any more and so I needed to go to a teacher who could take me further. I thought that sounded as if I was very good at playing the piano and so I was pleased to change teachers.

But it meant that I had to go into Hull on the bus every Saturday morning and it was half an hour each way. Then, when I got there, I had to catch a trolley bus which had two long metal prongs sticking up out of its top which went to wires above the road. They got electricity from the wires and that's how they moved. The top of the prongs kept following the wires when the bus turned, like a toy on sticks.

It was so hard to know where to get off and I peered out at the terrace houses, then at the old detached brick ones, hoping that I would recognise the bus stop in time. Sometimes, I got so panicky that I got off at a stop too early, then had to walk the rest of the way to Miss Brown's house, and I was late.

I had to knock and then go in, down a dark passage and into a big room with a grand piano and a bay window. If she had to wait for me, she was already at the piano, with her hands on her big lap covered in a pleated skirt. Her hair was a ginger colour and I couldn't help but notice that some of her scalp was the same colour. She always held a towelling rag in her hand to wipe the keys, when my sweaty hands made little dark blobs on the ivory. I felt ashamed then, but not as ashamed as when I was late. I knew that my lesson would be shorter, and I was wasting Mam's money.

And I felt I was wasting her money again when I went to play at the Hull music festival.

Miss Brown was a big believer in 'rising to the challenge'. But when I got home, I didn't practise much; and before I knew it the festival date had come. I hadn't risen to the challenge,

But nobody said anything and off we went on the bus. My mam and me were going to the new City Hall, in Hull. It had been bombed in the war and had been useless for years, but now it was so posh you couldn't believe it. Outside we were under the gaze of a big statue of Queen Victoria, she had public toilets underneath her and we nipped in there first. You had to go down steps underground, right under the Queen herself. The white shiny brick walls led into secret passages, like in the innards of the Queen.

I saw Ferens Art Gallery across the road and thought of how well my relative must have done to get his painting in there. I wished that I had seen it, but there was no time to think of that now, we were off into the big City Hall. I sat down on posh red upholstered chairs with the other kids that were going to play. They all had special music cases, but I just had my music book rolled up and I gripped it tight in my hands.

Then it all started, with speeches and clapping and kids going up to play on a grand piano – they were mostly girls in fluffy dresses but there were two boys in short trousers and black blazers. I had my Sunday school dress on – it was made by my mam from remnants. I sat there bored, until my name was called.

Then I got nervous. The piano was on a sort of wooden stage made of grey wood, there didn't seem to be any steps that I could see and suddenly, I didn't seem to be able to see anything much. I looked round in a daze, but all the spotlights were shining in my eyes. I scrambled up as best I could, then perched on the music stool and opened my music book to play the Mozart piece that I hadn't practised much. I peered at the notes on their lines and it seemed as if I couldn't read music at all. This wasn't true, of course, because I had been going to lessons for a few years now. I knew where the notes in my book were on the piano keys. But I sat there blinking and not knowing what to do, my heart was hammering, and all eyes must be on me. I had to do something.

I started to play, my rolled-up music book fell to the ground, but my fingers carried on playing the wonderful tune. As I swayed backward and forwards, I was not sure that I was playing all the correct notes, but I finished with the right chord and turned round smiling at the gloomy audience. Now, I noticed the steps at the side of the stage and walked off more easily than I had got on. Mam scowled and the adjudicator said, "I wonder what Mozart would think to the alterations in his masterpiece?" I should have practised some more.

On our way home, I went under Queen Victoria again, just to cool off in her marble innards. I know now that my piano playing will never be like Mam's.

Mam

Our Vi was no good at all at the music festival in Hull. She tried really hard, but I wished that I could go on stage and play the notes for her.

My own mother was a very good pianist. She had been brought up as a lady with her sisters and they could all play the piano and do embroidery. I liked playing duets with her, it was as if she trusted me and we played together as one person. Playing the piano came naturally to us both. Neither of us had lessons.

I have paid for piano lessons for my daughters. So far, they don't take after me with the piano. I used the family allowance to pay because I can do what I want with that and didn't have to ask Herb. He doesn't like music.

I have tried to get Vi and Gwendy to play a duet, but they wouldn't take it seriously and just kept on laughing.

Going to Hull reminded me of when I first got my job in Hull, but I didn't say anything to Vi. It was all such a long time ago. I am sure that she would not be interested.

After I was appointed to Madame Clapham's salon, I had to have a medical at a private clinic – it was a simple examination, and all was well. You needed to be well to work there as it was so cold and bare. There were no comforts for us workers. But I was lucky to be selected. I never forgot that.

I was in the beginners' room at first and had to do all sorts of easy jobs like sorting pins and needles and getting scraps of material from the floor. I was at the beck and call of all the experienced sewers. It was never ending, I worked till six at night. Before I left work, I covered all the unfinished sewing, which was on a long table, with a big white cotton cloth. Then I caught the bus from the George Street stop. It took about an hour to get home. There was hardly any time before I got up again at six in the morning to get ready and get the bus back to Hull. I had no idea that this job would end the way it did. I had such high hopes that I could do well here. Then one day I had a call.

"Madame says that you must go up to the room on the top floor." I was nervous, what could they want? I knew the embroidery room was on the top floor. Why would they want me there? No one explained, but at least I was not laid off, the woman in charge gave me some embroidery silks and needles. They must have been short of a woman that day I was called, but I didn't care about why. I just got on with the complicated stitches and sequins I had to sew on some cream silk fabric. I loved it; I was in my element doing this. I felt it was where I belonged. They must have liked my work because they called me again and again, until I was working in the embroidery room all the time.

"This is a very special job. The Salon has been commissioned to make a dress for the Princess Royal. You are to work on the bodice." I was told.

I was doing embroidery for royalty! This job could not get any better.

"There is no place for a mistake, so watch what you are doing."

The silk material was so fine, I bent my head over to concentrate. The design was marked out on tissue paper and I used pins to make light marks for the design. By my side was a page of drawings and instructions. Of course, I was supervised closely, and there were others doing the same job, but I was good enough to embroider for royalty. I felt so excited and proud – it was also nerve-wracking. My fingers began to sweat. A bowl of cold water and a towel was brought, and I was instructed to stop every ten minutes and rinse, then wipe my hands. I could have all the embroidery silks I needed in creams and fawns.

Day after day, I worked that bodice and it was truly beautiful. I was so proud when we had finished, I would have loved to see the completed dress, and it would have been even more wonderful to see the Princess Royal wearing the dress that I had worked on. But that was asking too much.

"I'm working on a dress for royalty!" I told my mother when I got home. She sat working on her own embroidery. The lamp was not very bright, but she knew her stitches well and sat close to the light. She smiled at me and reached out and stroked my arm.

"I am so pleased for you, Girly, remember this happiness."

She never had to go out to work because her father had always made a lot of money building houses. My father, her husband, always treated her like royalty and she always dressed in such fine clothes.

Back at work, I went automatically to the top room. I now had to work on embroidery on the sleeves of a dress for Queen Maud of Norway. I was embroidering for a queen! We never saw any royalty though; I suppose they could not mix with the likes of us workers.

In another room was a girl the same size as the Queen and a fitter was there, with her pins, to adjust the size. Then Madame Clapham was summoned to Sandringham with the dresses. They were all packed with tissue paper and folded on the long tables by experts who had done this before. Madame went with the dresses along with her top fitter. I never heard that they were not suitable, so I must have done good enough work.

I was working for a court dressmaker, but of course there were other well-to-do clients. If there was a ball in one of the big houses, we were working non-stop and I sometimes glanced through the crack in the door at the rich clients. Their room had beautiful curtains and soft furnishings, I was not allowed in there, of course, but it was enough for me to see it.

Things were going very well, and I lived in a fairy tale world of rich people and fine gowns. If I worked hard, I could get promotion and then who knew what could happen?

What happened was that my life at Madame Clapham's ended suddenly. Mother was poorly with the illness we were not allowed to mention. I was the eldest daughter and so I had to leave Madame Clapham's salon. I had to look after Mother as she lost her fight for life. She was taken into Hull infirmary by carriage. I hate to think of how the bumps in the road must have hurt her. The journey must have seemed never-ending. I went to see her.

"What time is it, Girly?" she asked. "I can't see a clock."

There was no clock and she was distressed because she had always lived by the clock. When to get up, when to have breakfast and all the other meals, then when to go out in her carriage.

"You can have this, Mother," I said leaning forwards and taking my gold watch off my own wrist to put on hers. It was so slack on her thin wrist that it swivelled round, with the heavy watch face underneath.

"Thank you, Girly," she said and smiled. That was the last time I saw her alive.

Suddenly, my dear, beautiful, loving mother was gone. My gold watch was given back to me in a brown envelope.

"At least she is free from pain," people said. "She is at peace." But the words were no comfort. I had not thought that this could happen. How could she die? How could she leave us all? My father was distraught. After the funeral he sat in front of the fire all day smoking his pipe in silence.

I did the cleaning and cooking without thinking – I was just empty. On the day that my mother died something beautiful inside me died with her.

"You can't go back to work," Father said. "Your brothers and little sister need you here now." What could I do? I had to give up the idea of the job of my dreams for ever. I had to look after my father and my youngest sister and little brothers who were still at home. That's when my father developed agoraphobia and he could not go out of the door, so he was pretty helpless without me.

I did my duty and sacrificed everything. In a few months I had to grow up fast and be the 'mother' to the children and look after my father, who was grief stricken. I just had to get on with it and do my best. What else could I do?

It was a blessing, really, that I had to keep busy because it stopped me thinking about what had happened and what I had lost. I prayed to God every day to give me strength to carry on.

Herb came to see me, and we walked hand in hand in the garden or down Green Lane. It gave me comfort to be with him.

I could understand our king wanting to be with the love of his life, but I do not hold with divorce. When you marry it is forever, after all that is what you promise. Wallis had been married and was not free. What an awful choice for Edward, I didn't know whose side to be on. In the end we lost our king, he abdicated to be with his true love. He left his family; it would be as if they had died. Love or duty? I couldn't decide, but it wasn't my decision.

My decision was to look after my brothers and sisters.

It helped when I saw Herb. He was strong and steady. He knew what it was like to have death in the family. Two of his beloved sisters had died within a year of each other. Both were so young and full of life, but they caught tuberculosis, and nothing could be done to save them. They were buried side by side with lily-white marble headstones in the churchyard at Gum. That was five years ago, but I knew that my mother's death must have brought it all back to him. We sat on the garden seat, holding hands, in silence.

I played my mother's piano in the evening. Sometimes Peggy played a duet with me, but it wasn't the same.

After a year or so I started going dancing again on Saturday nights at Ringam village hall. We danced well together. Herb was very agile as a dancer; I suppose it was because he was so active as a farmer. We loved waltzing – moving together like one person. We did the foxtrot, but Herb would not dance the Charleston, he thought it too modern.

Then, when we had been engaged for four years, we decided it was time we got married. My sister and brothers did not need me as much now they were older, they could look after themselves more easily. I told them that I would always be on hand for them if they needed me. It was the least I could do. I felt that my job in life was to take care of them. I had no mother to advise me and help me or be proud of me. I had to make my own decisions now.

I decided we had waited long enough. But Herb had to consider the farm and his brother, who worked with him. He had to wait until the harvest was over and then we were able to get married, before lambing started.

There was one thing that was bothering me, though –

"Herb, I've just thought. There is no piano in your house, I will miss it so much." I could not take Mother's piano from my sisters. They would get comfort from it when they played it.

"We'll have to get you one then," he answered, and that is what we did.

One day, when he had an hour or so to spare, we went into Hull and bought a second hand one from a reputable music shop. I was so pleased – I could not bear to break that link with my mother.

Our wedding was on a cold day in November at Ringam chapel, where all my family worshipped and where my own dead mother had married. My young sister, Kathy, was a bridesmaid along with Herb's young sister, Milly. Sid was Herb's best man.

I made my own white fitted dress. I made the flowing veil, as well as the two bridesmaid dresses in gold satin. Milly and Kathy made their own little hats. Millie's was a crown. She had used cardboard and cut it to size. She covered the whole thing with gold material, then stuck glass 'jewels' on. I suppose she got the ideas from the department store – Willis Ludlow where she had just started work in Hull. She really did look like a princess.

Herb paid for my flowers and he chose big yellow chrysanthemums. I felt so beautiful and special.

We went to Scarborough for our honeymoon. What a shock the cold blast was – it came from the North Sea, with nothing to stop it. In fact, it was all a bit of a shock, I had a rude awakening you could say, I had no idea what was in store for me.

Chapter 8

Playing the game

Me

At my Ripsea school we had to play games. Not games that you wanted to play, like on our farm, but games that they told you to play. In the summer we had to play netball, and in the winter, we played hockey.

For netball our playground had all the markings you needed, painted in yellow lines. Netball wasn't so bad. I had made a new friend – a girl called Sandra. I had seen her at primary school, but had never got to know her, and now she had come up with me to the prestigious 'A' class. She was sort of old fashioned and wore skirts below her knees and lived in a little far -away village called Humberside. Every day she had to cycle down a long road to Ringam to catch the school bus. Sandra was pretty strong, I guess it was from all that cycling, and she was tall. She was very good at playing netball. She was goal shooter and scored a lot of goals for our side, because she was so tall, she was nearer the net on a pole than any of the others. She was in the semicircle ready to shoot. I was at the other end and couldn't go in the semicircles, but I could try and stop the other team getting the ball there. I wasn't tall like Sandra, but I could duck and dive, and be there to stop the ball getting to the enemy team. It was harder if it was windy, which it usually was, because the east wind caught the ball.

The wind was the enemy to Sandra, when she was on her bike trying to get the school bus on time. If it was head wind blowing across the salt marshes, then she was in trouble. It took her twice as long and she had to be on time, there was no second chance – there was only one school bus.

"At least it will be back wind going home," she said, but of course, during the day the wind could change, and it was still a head wind on her journey back.

The wind changed for me in winter, when we had to play hockey instead of netball and, even worse, we had to have a shower after playing. We only had a bath at home, and I love our new bathroom even though it was big and cold. I had a bath on Sundays. Showers frightened me.

Also, with hockey you had to wear some special shorts. They had to be bought through the school outfitter shop at Ripsea, and Mam wasn't allowed to make them like she could for netball. My hockey shorts were navy – that was the school colour – everything had to be navy, even our bus was navy. They were made of very thick material and were pleated with a joining bit of material between my legs. Mine were too big. I suppose it was so that I could wear them next year, but it was so cold on our field and I was so skinny that, at this rate, I didn't think I would be around for next year – at least not playing hockey.

You also had to wear big thick socks (navy) going up to your knee – mine went over my knees – and hockey boots with studs in. It took us so long to get dressed, we used to take part of the lesson time up, which is what I wanted. I hated hockey and I was no good at it.

We had to pick teams. I only just managed to scrape into a netball team, but now I stood there with a fixed grin on my face while the hockey team leaders picked. Who picked the team leaders? That's what I wanted to know. Well, I could guess really because they would be picked by Miss Legg our PE teacher. Both girls were big and tall and strong – I would have picked them – anybody would.

'Pick me, pick me,' I wanted to say as I stood there longing to be picked, but they didn't pick me, and I was left with some other 'spares' to practise at the bottom of the field while the teams played a real game. We didn't know how to practise, nobody told us what to do – I was never going to get in the team at this rate. Oh, and there was the hockey stick, of course we had to have a stick. I hadn't got one. Well that isn't true, I had one to use – it was Mam's old one – from when she was young. Katy had used it and then our Gwendy gave it a go, but it was an old fashioned one and had no springs – it made your hands really sting if you hit the hard ball. So, Mam persuaded Dad to buy a new stick.

"Gwendy needs a new hockey stick, Herb," she said.

"What's wrong with your old one? It was good enough for Katy."

"Yes, but it's at least twenty-five years old – a quarter of a century."

And so, after a lot of persuasion a new stick was bought – but I never got it – I don't know where it went, but it didn't come to me. We think somebody borrowed it from Gwendy and it never came back. Anyway, by the time it was my turn for hockey, it was back to using Mam's old stick. The rubber cover was rotting from when it was kept in our under-stairs cupboard, but that is all there was. Mam didn't think Dad would buy another. So, I got dressed in this outfit and went off to practise with Mam's old stick.

At night, I heard Mam and Uncle Sid whispering again.

"Wsss, wsss, wsss."

I bet they were whispering about how bad I was at games at school.

Mam was good at hockey, so I thought I would give it a try. Once, when loads of girls were off school poorly with flu and I had just got back from being poorly myself, there was nobody else to choose, so I was given a place. I was left wing. This was my chance at last, but left wing has to run up and down the whole pitch, and by the time I got there, the ball was back at the other end. I was no good.

After we had finished hockey, we had to have a shower. Miss Legg loved us having showers. She liked netball, hockey, athletics and gymnastics but most of all she liked the showers.

She sat cross legged on the gym floor – with her hockey shorts on – and told us about the showers that had been put in at the back of our new gym.

"You must bring a shower cap and towel," she said. You could be excused a shower with a letter from your mam, if it was your time of the month, but you couldn't have two 'times of the month' in one month, if you see what I mean.

We got stripped and stood in a line with our shower caps on – Aunty Peggy bought me one from a posh ladies' shop in Hull, it was rubbery and had blue flowers on it.

Then the water came on and we had to go in this horseshoe shaped corridor with pipes all round it squirting cool water.

"Move, girls walk around, don't just stand there," shouted Miss Legg, watching us from a distant dry part.

I didn't look up, I kept on looking at my feet. I never looked as high as the others' shower caps – I wonder if they were school navy. Was I the only one with a flowery cap?

I hated having showers, I dreaded games on Fridays, and when Friday was over, I went home happy and looking forward to the weekend. But Monday came round, then soon it was Thursday and I dreaded tomorrow.

Sandra didn't seem to mind games and showers too much. Mam said Sandra 'took things in her stride.' And that was because she had older parents who had to let her get on with things. She was a 'late baby' and so her mam and dad were in their sixties. I couldn't help thinking of our late baby that had died.

I went to see Sandra once or twice at Humberside. She lived in a little brick house in a row with a few others. I went on the bus to Ringam, and she biked down to meet me, then she walked back with me. She wheeled her bike at the side. When we got there, we didn't play, Sandra was too grown up for that, but we did talk outside on a seat in their little garden and then there were sandwiches for tea.

Me and my Mam

After that she walked me back to Ringam wheeling her bike, which she could ride home. I hoped it wasn't a head wind.

Before she left, she said, "I have been picked for the school hockey team."

"You must be very good at it," I said.

"Fairly good, I think."

I told Mam and she said that Sandra was very modest. I didn't see the point – if I was good at hockey, I would say so, especially if Mam could hear me. But I wasn't good at hockey.

Mam

It is strange to see my stick being used again. I stored my hockey stick in our under-stairs cupboard – until Katy discovered it when she needed it.

I let the girls have it and I didn't say anything, but I truly loved that stick and the fun I had when I played.

I enjoyed games and athletics and I think that I was fairly good at both. I was slim and healthy, and I liked competing. Peggy and I used to practise on the cricket grounds at Ringam. We were both reasonable players and we got in the village team. Peggy was working as a secretary and I still had a little money saved from Madame Clapham's.

"Let's buy our own sticks," said Peggy and that is what we did. I felt so pleased to be doing something for myself. I could run and I played left wing.

I made our outfits – just a simple navy, knee length skirt and a white shirt each. We wore our lace-up shoes because we couldn't afford special boots. The other girls copied and made their own outfits. We loved wearing them it made us so proud to be part of the team. We practised on Saturday mornings when we could, but we were not allowed on Sunday, as it was a day of rest. It was a holy day when we had a bath in front of the fire. We wore our Sunday best and went to Chapel.

"We won!" shouted Peggy after a game with the Sunkstead team and we held our sticks in the air. The other team was from

78

a village smaller than Ringam and everybody had expected we would win, but even so it was an achievement and we were so pleased.

When I got married at Ringam the whole hockey team came. It was a lovely surprise and even bigger surprise when they rushed out before me and made a tunnel of hockey sticks for me to walk through with Herb holding my hand.

After I was married, I did not play hockey again. I was too busy looking after the farmhouse, which had big rooms. And of course, I had to look after Herb and do my jobs on the farm. Then, I was in the family way fairly quickly. It was all quite frightening really, and I hadn't got my own mother to help or give advice.

We lived in what had been the servants' quarter and the door between us and the main house was blocked with an old bookcase. There was some more old mahogany furniture already there – it was all big and solid. I would have liked to buy my own, but of course, that was out of the question.

Lilian, Herb's mother, was next door, but one of her daughters was really poorly and I didn't like to bother her. It was her youngest, Milly, the one that had been our bridesmaid. So, I just kept quiet and managed as best I could. I got on with it and let things happen.

Our Katy was born after a long labour – well they say that the first is the worst. Then, I didn't really know how to look after her. Mother had always bought help in when my brothers and sisters were born, so I didn't know much about looking after small babies.

There wasn't anybody to ask when I had mine. None of my brothers or sisters had children yet, so I just did my best. I felt so alone and desperate when baby Katy cried. I didn't know what to do.

But what had I to complain about? Nothing, especially when Herb's sister died. Milly was the youngest and I think she was a bit of a favourite with them all. Little Milly was dead of consumption. How could she be? She had been so full of life and fun and then she got so thin and went to bed coughing and she just slipped quietly away one night. The third daughter to die. She was buried in another lily-white marble grave next to her two sisters at Gum church. Our little princess had gone.

"Three of our lasses buried," said Herb. "I used to have six sisters." Then he rushed out to feed his animals.

I don't know how his mother carried on. But you do, don't you?

"Come and see baby Katy," I said to her one day, when little Katy was asleep in her pram, looking so angelic. I thought that it would cheer Lilian up and that new life would bring her some joy.

"I don't want to see your baby," she said. "I have just buried my youngest daughter and I can't think of anything else." I did not know what to say.

I went back to our house and cried. Baby Katy woke up and she cried as well. I picked her up and rocked her backwards and forwards with my tears falling on hers.

But, one way or other, we all just kept putting one step in front of another. Then when I thought that things could not get any worse, the war started. I think that was when my hockey stick got pushed to the back of the under-stairs cupboard. There was no time for fun and games then.

I know the showers are not popular at Ripsea school but really, they are lucky to have them. We always had to get a wash -down at the kitchen sink and only had a tin bath in front of the fire every week. The hot water came from the tank at the side of the fire. I used to ladle it into the bath and the girls took it in turn to get in every Sunday. But then, at last, a bathroom with running hot and cold water was planned for us. Grandma and Vera next door were to have one, as well.

I was in my element at first. It was to be partitioned from our bedroom, which is huge and could easily be cut down in size. New walls were put in with plasterboard and new plumbing. What a mess it all was!

I whispered to Sid about all the noise and dust. I didn't want to complain, but really all that noise and dust was too much.

As it turned out though, the new bathroom is a boon. It has a handbasin and a big airing cupboard and there is a separate flush toilet in a room next to it. The old-fashioned fireplace was taken away and a new one with a back boiler was put in to supply the water for the bathroom. Pity it didn't go to my wash house, because there is no hot supply there and I still have to use my 'copper' to heat the water. But never mind, I am grateful for my modern bathroom. I even chose the wallpaper. It had to be special water-resistant paper so there wasn't much of a selection from the hardware shop at Ringam, but I am pleased with the effect. It all looks so good.

Chapter 9

Appearances

Me

My mam said that appearances were important, and she always dressed us girls in clean clothes, when we went out. She made my blouse for Ripsea school and she knitted me a new navy skirt. I didn't match the others in my class because they all went to the special outfitter in Ripsea to get their uniform. My knitted skirt was very droopy, but I was clean and tidy.

"You're not very with it," said Brenda, who knew what there was to know about fashion and how to look good.

'If Mam keeps on making all my clothes, then I will never be with it,' I thought. But Mam did keep making all my clothes, using any piece of remnant she could get hold of. I was clean and tidy, but I wanted to be 'with it' and be like the others in my class whose parents went to the uniform shop.

At Ripsea school we had moved from the huts after our first year – we had a different form teachers and rooms in the main building. It was much better because we didn't have to run every morning to be on time for assembly. We just had to queue up at the classroom door then walk down the corridor on the left-hand side. When we got there, we waited for the new first year to come running from the huts, just like we had once.

Now, our form teacher was called Mr Hellas, he taught us English, and he lived in the library. Well, it seemed as if he lived in the library because except for dinner time I never saw him anywhere else. He walked about with a black gown on, and inside one of the big long arm drapes was a stick. I knew this because when he turned around one arm flap moved stiffly (the one with the stick) but the other flapped gently by his side. And to make matters worse, he held his head in the air as if he was looking at the ceiling all the time. We all laughed at him behind his back, because he looked so strange, but secretly we were a bit frightened of him. Then one day something happened which stopped me laughing at him once and for all.

Mr Hellas sent for me. I was in my French class. A lad came in our room and said, "Mr Hellas wants Victoria to come straight away." So of course, Mademoiselle let me go. I don't think even she wanted to upset Mr Hellas.

When I got there, Mr Hellas beckoned me to the front of the class.

"What is another name for the wood anemone? With it." He always said, 'With it' at the end of every sentence. But he didn't mean that we were with it and looked good. I don't think that he meant anything. Mam said it was a bit like a tic, just a habit he got into and couldn't get out of.

Well, his question was easy, I thought that everybody knows that answer, because it is such a lovely little flower and it bobs about in the wind. There are loads of them in our wood.

"It is called the windflower, sir."

"There we are – someone who truly knows the countryside, with it."

I heard some sniggering, but I didn't know what that was about.

"Dismissed, with it."

And off I went back to French lessons, and I went with a smile, because even though I was not dressed like everyone else I felt 'with it' today. And I was not frightened of Mr Hellas, even though he looked and behaved strangely. He knew about me – he knew I knew about the countryside.

Mr Hellas had a lot of rules to make sure the appearance of the library was always good. He was like Mam that way. He cared about things being clean and tidy. We must not put our satchels on the tables in the library. The tops were nearly white, they were smooth and were polished with 'lavendo', said Mr Hellas. I think that he did it himself when we went home. There was always a duster and a tin of purple polish on his ice smooth table, where he sat. But the good appearances did not make me good at handwriting.

Mam had top marks for good, neat handwriting and she always wrote Dad's letters for him. I don't think my dad could write. At least, I never saw him write. He didn't even write his own cheques. He couldn't see close to, either. He could see at a distance, but he couldn't read a newspaper now, without glasses, and he wouldn't have his eyes tested. He said that his eyes were good enough for his needs.

I used to go to Hull market with him and watch when he had to pay for beast that he had bought. He signed a blank cheque and then handed his cheque book over to the seller and said, "Here. Fill this in." The man filled it in, then tore out the cheque.

"How do you know he won't cheat you?" I gasped. "He might write more pounds than it should be, and you have signed it."

"He would only do it once," said Dad and rushed on to his next job at the market.

One day, I was with Dad when we went to Beverley market, we usually went to Hull but today there had been a change of plan and our cattle went to Beverley. He hadn't had time to put his cavalry twills on or his tweed jacket with his trilby. He was in his old farming clothes and cap. Mam rushed to get his good shoes and hat, but he wasn't having any of it and brushed her away.

He should have listened because his bad appearance left us in a bit of trouble. He wasn't as well-known at Beverley as he was in Hull. And another thing was, he had to go to the bank and get cash for our workers' wages. All went well at first, and we sold our cattle for a good price. Now for the bank. As soon as Dad went in, I saw a cashier go round the back of the wooden cubicle. Everybody stopped talking and when it was Dad's turn to get his money, he signed a cheque and then handed it over to the cashier to fill in.

"Fill it in for £50," said Dad. The cashier took the cheque and asked us to wait. It was ages before the manager came out with the cashier.

"I will have to phone your bank in Hull, to verify who you are, before we can give you this money. It is a great deal and you look..."

Dad stood still and stared. The cashier scurried back behind the counter with his head down and the manager, in his black suit and white shirt, marched off to his office to ring their main Hull bank.

Dad stood stock still in the middle of the polished floor and I stood by his side. People started to stare at this short, unshaven worker and they walked around us giving plenty of room in between.

Dad stood upright and looked ahead, without blinking.

I began to feel embarrassed; they were all thinking Dad should not be in the bank trying to cash a cheque. They were all thinking that my dad did not have the money. I shuffled uneasily.

Dad didn't move.

Then all of a sudden, the manager came out of his office in a flurry.

"Come this way, sir, I will personally cash the cheque for you. How would you like it, sir?"

"In notes," said my dad not flinching, not moving.

"£10 notes, sir?" the manager bowed.

"As it comes," said Dad still standing in the middle of the floor.

The manager backed off and ran into his office, rushing back after a second or two with his fist full of notes.

"Three tens, sir, and one, two, three, four fives." He counted them out into Dad's hand.

"Thank you," said my dad. His face was as steady as a rock as he pocketed the money.

My dad turned to go. I followed him, and the manager rushed to the door to open it for us.

We walked out as steadily as we had walked in and got in our van and drove home.

We never knew the conversation that the Beverley bank manager had with the Hull manager, but Dad thought it was something like this –

"Hello, Mr Clark, this is the manager of the Beverley bank."

"What's the problem?"

"I have a man here who is trying to cash a £50 cheque."

"Did he write the cheque?"

"No, the man signed a blank cheque, then the cashier wrote it. It seems very suspicious to me."

"What does he look like?"

"Well hard to describe. Not very tidy and..."

"Like a tramp would you say?"

"Yes, exactly."

"Give him the money, and hurry, he is one of our best customers."

Mam never laughed at this joke, but Dad did. I laughed with Dad, but Mam thought he was too bad going into a bank without thinking of his appearance.

Then that week we had to write a composition for Mr 'with it' Hellas, with the title 'A Cathedral Town'. I didn't know a cathedral town. Mam said that she thought the nearest was York. I hadn't been to York. What could I do?

"Maybe you could write about Beverley, you have been there, and it has a minster."

So that is what I did. I started to write about Beverley. But the sentences would not come. I could not squeeze them out with the ink from my fountain pen.

'Beverley has a minster. I have been to Beverley on Wednesday with my dad.' I began but didn't know how to go on. I did not know Beverley. Mam said that there were narrow winding streets – she was ironing. We were working on our big table. She was at one end and I was at the other.

'Beverley has narrow winding streets.'

"And you know that there is a cattle market – you have just been with your dad."

'Beverley has a cattle market, that is why I went with my dad.'

No more could be forced out of my pen. I knew about the windflower, but I didn't know about a cathedral town.

Mam folded her ironing away neatly and looked over my shoulder, she didn't think my composition was very special. Worst of all, it wasn't neat and tidy, I had done some crossing out and a blot came, when I was thinking. Mam wants everything to look good and this did not look good.

Mam

They said that I had neat handwriting at school and now I write all the letters that Herb needs. He hates writing letters. Whenever he had written one in the past, he rushed so much he didn't take time to make himself clear. We even had one of his letters sent back saying that they did not understand his request. So, now I enjoy doing it and it saves him the time and effort. I write to the bank, I order things he needs, I send animal records off to the authorities and things like that. Herb can't be bothered with neat handwriting; he only wants to work with his animals. He cannot be bothered with how he looks either so long as he can get on with his work.

I think I got my idea of how appearances matter from the war. It was all we could do to keep up appearances. If we let things go, we would have been finished. What was happening did not bear thinking about. It started just after our Katy was born and Milly died.

"They're out, they're out," shouted the air raid warden coming on his bike from Ringam. We were too far away to hear a siren. I had my baby in my arms, when I first had to run to the air raid shelter at the bottom of our orchard. Sid and Herb built it. They made it with tin sheets and lined it with straw bales.

"Here you are. That'll keep you both warm," said Herb as he carefully wrapped a grey blanket round me and the baby.

"And I've lit the oil lamp, look." There were no windows so the light could not be seen. If we had been in our house, we would have had to put the shutters up, Sid had got a joiner to make them. I would have had to draw the blackout curtains that I had made, as well. But tonight, it was too dangerous to be in the house.

Sid saw to Grandma – we all called Lilian 'Grandma' now after all she had been through with three dead daughters. Somehow, we wanted to show how we respected her and 'Grandma' instead of 'Lilian' seemed right. We wanted to show her that she was important to us all, even though she could not be a mother to all her daughters now.

We sat all night. Sid and Herb were off at dawn to see to the animals. We tried to sleep but we were cold and uncomfortable.

You would think that our farm, at the end of a long country lane, would have been the safest of places. Safer than Ringam, where my sisters lived. But it was not, you see at the end of our field and beyond a strip of trees, there were some BBC transmitters – they were tall masts and they sent the Home Service radio programmes into Europe. I suppose they were dangerous for our enemies because it helped our troops to know all the good things about home and made them stronger. Also, of course, messages could be sent. So, the transmitters were a target for German aircraft bombers and our farm was in the flight path of the bombs. It wasn't long before soldiers were billeted at Grandma's (she had even more room now she had lost three daughters) and anti-aircraft guns were positioned in our fields. Things were happening so fast and we hardly had time to take it all in.

Then a little boy evacuee called Billy, and his mother, Ivy, came to live with us from Hull. It was a lot worse for them in

Hull, the city was bombed to smithereens. I suppose the Germans were trying to put the docks out of action. Ivy and Billy came with their own gas masks.

'Good heavens,' I thought, 'surely they won't gas us down here, down our lane in the darkness?'

All our life was turned up-side-down. Our farm workers signed up and went to fight. We were given two land girls to do some of the work, but the rest was up to us. If we gave in to fear, we would have come to a standstill. My one comfort was that my brother Teddy came to work on the farm. He had only just left school and was too young to fight. At least I could keep an eye on him.

But nothing was our own any more, all we had was our pride and our ability to keep going and keep up appearances. And I was determined. We kept going, by putting one foot in front of another and getting on with our work. I made little things matter – I scrubbed the stone floors and tried to keep the workers off it.

"Will you stand on the paper I have put down?" I asked impatiently as one of the lads or one of the land girls came in. We had a darts board on the back of our room door and they sometimes came to play. It had to be just after our dinner because that's when they had half an hour left before working again. It was no good waiting until teatime, you could not see clearly enough, what with the blackout curtains and shutters. They all got good at darts and played every day – even the soldiers liked playing. I suppose it was a bit of a distraction from all that we were going through.

"How can I keep this floor clean if you come in with dirty boots?" It was no good talking to them about the ugly holes left in the wooden door if the dart missed the target.

Grandma reacted to the war and the loss of her daughters by having the cleanest and whitest washing. She spent all Monday on it.

"Don't go in the orchard, I have just hung my washing out," she told the soldiers impatiently. I suppose she thought that they might get it dirty if they played a game of football and kicked it into her whiter than white bleached, hanging clothes.

Appearances were very important in those days. It was our way of taking some control and I still think appearances are important.

Chapter 10

In service

Me

We had a lot of 'subjects' to study at Ripsea. They were all very different and some, like French, were very strange to me. But one subject I thought would be easy was sewing. I had seen Mam do this all the time and I had learnt some stitches. I also knew how to use a sewing machine because I had watched how Mam did it.

Well, the first thing we had to make was a pair of knickers. The boys did not do this, of course, they were down another corridor where we girls did not go – they were doing woodwork and metalwork when we did sewing and cooking. But we weren't onto cooking yet – we were sewing.

A big surprise, to me, was that our knickers were not navy – we were making gingham knickers – blue and white squared gingham.

There seemed to be only one size. We had to share the pattern, cut out in tracing paper. I was quite small, but I had to have the same size as all the big girls in my class. Sandra had the same size as me and she was much taller. Our teacher Miss Pole was quite round. I wonder if it was her pattern for her knickers when she was young. Anyway, there was no chance of asking about it, we just had to get on and cut our pattern out. There were two sides the same – front and back, and then there was a gusset which had to be double – so we cut two of those as well. We cut our material off a bale of fabric Miss Pole gave us, and our mams had to send half a crown to pay for it. It seemed a lot of money, but we were buying enough material to make a pinny as well.

I had to concentrate on making my knickers first. There was a sewing machine to share between each group. We had to join the gusset, then stitch the sides. After that we did all the hemming by hand. Lastly, we threaded the elastic through. It took us a long time to finish. I was quick on the sewing machine, but some girls didn't know how to thread it and they took ages. I took ages with the hems, my hands kept getting sweaty and the thread got wet and wouldn't pull through. When we had finished, we had to look forward to the pinnies.

"Now, girls, we are ready to make our aprons, we will also be making a stand-up hat to keep your hair away from food and cuffs to keep your sleeves out of the way."

I never wore those knickers (Mam said that they were 'voluminous', and she was not too pleased). But I had to wear my 'apron'.

You see, we had to serve the teachers, and to do this we had to wear an apron, cuffs and a waitress hat. The pattern was too big for me again, and so Miss Pole said to shorten it by folding it over just above the hem. To hide the fold, I had to embroider it. I did stars and chevrons, with French knots and blanket stitch. I had learnt them all from Mam's book (which was supposed to be mine now). I plodded on, and even took it home to get it done faster. (Mam didn't like it – I should have cut it to length before I hemmed it, she said.)

We had to serve the teachers next term. Mam threaded the elastic in my cuffs and starched my waitress hat, which I tied with two white threads at the back of my head. And now I was ready for the teachers.

Nobody told us what to do, we just had to get our outfit on and stand in the dining room at the top, near the windows where the teachers' table was. The cooks brought the trolley, with the food covered in metal lids then the teachers came and sat down. They didn't look at us or speak to us. They just laughed and talked to each other. Mr Hellas didn't speak to anybody and they did not speak to him. He came with his black gown and sat down with his head in the air. I was with Sandra and we started to unload the dishes and put them on the teachers' tables. Then we had to put green plates in front of them.

"Go to their left," whispered Sandra, "always go to the left." So that's what I did. I learnt not to be a nuisance and to try and be invisible as I bobbed about in silence giving food to our teachers and scraping away their left-overs. Sandra was really good at it and she looked as if she knew what she was doing. Her blonde curls curved over the side of her waitress hat. As I have said, she was tall, and she could calmly reach over their shoulders, while I had to go under their arms.

Once, I bumped into Mr Hellas' elbow and knocked his arm, when he was trying to get a drink. Water went everywhere, and I didn't know what to do. The head cook saw though and came out with a cloth to mop up. She had a white wrap-around apron on with white cuffs to hold her sleeves up, but she didn't have a hat on like me. She mopped up without looking at me. With a few swipes of her string-knitted cloth the water was gone.

Sandra carried on serving as if nothing had happened. Mr Hellas never looked at me, and I never looked at him — just get on with the job, I thought, it will soon be over.

But there was another job we had to learn to do, and that was to serve the Headmaster, Mr Sparrow. One of us had to go to his office and ask what he wanted to eat. He had a choice of puddings. It was my turn to ask.

"Ask him if he wants Spotty Dick or cheese and biscuits," said the head cook in her 'not looking at you' voice.

I went along the carpeted teachers' corridor. You were not allowed to go here normally, but in my serving outfit I was allowed. I knocked on the door and waited for him to shout, 'come in'.

"Do you want Spotty Dick or cheese and biscuits?" I blurted as soon as I got in, I didn't know what Spotty Dick was.

"What colour is the custard with Spotty Dick?" he asked, not looking up from his big desk covered with papers.

"I don't know, sir."

He looked up then and smiled a flat smile.

"I'd better have cheese and biscuits to be on the safe side."

"He wants cheese and biscuits," I told the cook.

"That's funny, he normally likes Spotty Dick." She gave me a slab of cheese on a plate with two Ryvitas. I took it to him.

Then I had to take his tea on a tray. The tray was heavy, with a big metal teapot and a green cup and saucer with a milk jug and sugar basin to match. I couldn't knock on the door – I had no free hand, so I put the tray on the carpet and knocked. When I heard him shout, "Come in," I opened the door and then bent to pick up the tray. I put it on his table and stood next to him while he poured. He put his arm round me.

"Is it Virginia?" he asked. At first, I didn't know what he meant. I looked at him and he was looking at the teapot, so I thought he must be talking about the tea. I knew that there was a tea called Virginia Tea, but I didn't really know if this was it. I made a guess.

"Yes," I answered and then dashed for the door.

"Thank you, Virginia," he said.

Oh no! He must have thought I was called Virginia. I escaped and galloped down the carpeted corridor in shame.

I am not going to tell Mam about it.

Mam

There was a young girl, in service at Grandma's. She lived there and did the washing and the cleaning before the war. I hoped my girls didn't have to do that. But there was Vi serving the teachers now. I don't like it very much, but I didn't say anything to her.

The girl soon left Grandma, once the war started, she went to the war effort. She signed up as a Wren. Then our Peggy joined her. One of my brothers joined the army the others were too young. So, I know all about being in service and I was lucky that I had my work cut out here and didn't have to leave. I was certainly doing my bit for the war effort, looking after Ivy and her little boy. Her husband came from Hull sometimes at the weekend and he had to be fed, as well.

Then, an even more dreadful thing happened. Another of Herb's sisters, Lily, next door started to cough. She coughed and coughed and could not stop. It was only a year after dear little Milly had died. It couldn't be happening again, surely? I heard Lily slam the door and rush outside, standing on the cobbles she coughed as if she would never stop. She must have been cold out there, especially as she had got so thin, but she would not want to upset her mother. Then she started coughing blood. One day, I saw her through the window looking into her hanky. And I saw the bright red stain. But she would not give in.

"Come and sit with me, in our house, Lily," I said.

"No, thank you. I'll go back to Mother when the coughing stops," she said.

The weary winter months wore on, Lily lost even more weight and she looked so pale. But still she carried on helping her mother in the house. None of us said anything about it. We dare not.

We carried on into the spring. Lily was twenty-six and had the strength of the young. We were hopeful. And now the wild flowers were out in the hedgerow and the trees were in leaf, things did not seem, so bleak. She rallied and started going for short walks. God had taken mercy on us, at last.

But our relief was short lived, and Lily took to her bed. I went to see her. Her beautiful black hair was spread on the whiter than white pillowcase. Grandma sat with her and Doctor Moon was sent for.

"She needs plenty of rest," he said, "and get her to the seaside if you can. The sea air will be beneficial."

He left some medicine which helped with the pain, but we could not get her to the seaside where the pure air could have helped. She was too weak and there was an air raid that night and I sat in the shelter with my little girl, and Grandma sat at Lily's bedside.

We had borne enough, especially Grandma. Our lives were blacker than the blackouts.

We did what we could, but Lily died all the same.

Now there were four white marble graves in Gum churchyard. How could we bear this sorrow? It didn't seem possible. Dear God, would you please send a bomb, drop it on us and put us all out of our misery?

A bomb didn't drop on us and we all kept going, somehow. Me with my scrubbing and cleaning, and Grandma washing and bleaching.

I fell pregnant again, I felt so guilty, with Grandma losing her fourth daughter. But there was no stopping it and I was soon showing, I didn't say anything, but I could do something to help. It was only a small thing, I decided to make Grandma's indoor hats for her. She always wore a little cap with a turn-up round her face. It kept her long grey hair neat and tidy.

"I've made you two indoor bonnets, Grandma," I said offering her the two blue caps. She didn't say anything.

"I know you haven't been able to buy any this year what with the war, and I thought you would want them." She looked at me and took them onto her lap. She sat holding them and staring into space. Eventually she started stroking them gently, smoothing them out with her flat hand. I hoped she liked them, it was the least I could do.

My pregnancy and birth were all much simpler this time, as I knew what would happen, but the war complicated things and I worried about a midwife getting to me in time. As it happened, it was an easy birth and there was no air raid. I had another baby girl. I did not mind when I saw how perfect and beautiful she was. But I knew Herb wanted a boy.

Then Vera, one of the land girls fell in love with Sid. She was only young, but she was strong and knew her own mind. She was from Hessle Road in Hull and they were known for being tough, what with their men working on the docks and in the fishing boats in the rough North Sea.

Sid and Vera were married in Hull, it was a war time wedding and she could not have what I had for mine, but she looked so happy. Vera's first baby was a boy.

The war carried on and on. A bomb dropped in one of our fields. The anti-aircraft guns missed their target – so did the German plane and the bomb fell on a willow tree. We watched from the air raid shelter as it burnt – a huge light in a black sky.

I feared for my little girls and hugged them to me.

I was worried again about how we would manage, but Herb said that the war was good for the farm. It's awful to say that, when there was so much suffering. But he and Sid were able to plough up more fields to grow more crops and there was extra money for each acre. We had subsidies for drainage and fertilizers.

"We have a lot to thank WarAg for," said Herb.

"What's that?"

"It's a government department that gives money to us farmers if we do what they say."

"I suppose we have to feed the nation, but it doesn't seem right that we make money out of the war."

"We are doing our bit to support the nation," said Herb, and it was true they worked all hours, and so did Vera and me.

Chapter 11

Making mistakes

Me

Our Gwendy had joined the school choir as soon as she went to Ripsea. I thought that I had better give it a go. You had to turn up after school on Monday, Mam was a good singer I heard her at chapel singing all the hymns, as she played the organ for the service. She sort-of warbled and her voice had a trembling in it. It sounded good.

I had sung before in Singing Together at primary school with Mr Bantam — our headmaster. He really liked William Appleby; whose voice taught us from the wireless. I looked forward to the lesson and we all sang folk songs. We had the music books in front of us and they had little drawings in, as well as the notes and the words.

Now for a proper choir. This time, I was allowed down the boys' metalwork and woodwork corridor, and right at the end was a big music room. The new pupils going into our choir had to sing on their own. You had to choose a song that you knew and sing it. I stood in a line. Mr Jackson tapped each one of us on the shoulder in turn, and when he did, we had to sing our chosen song. He bent down and put his hand to his ear and put his ear to your mouth. I was at the end of the row and watched what was happening.

My throat suddenly went dry. I couldn't think of anything to sing. Then I remembered Uncle Sid used to sing Perry Como's song, in the morning when he came into our house. It was about catching a star and keeping it safe because there might be rain the next night and no stars to see.

I sang that as best I could, and I put a little warble in it like Mam does.

"Do you know that song?" asked Mr Jackson. I didn't know what he meant, of course I knew that song. I sang it didn't I?

"Shall I sing some more? I know all the words."

But he wasn't listening – he had moved away.

He put me with the altos.

Sopranos were on one side and altos on the other. The lads were all at the back. Then we started singing. There were four different parts to sing, but I only had to sing alto. We sang '*The Elizabethan Serenade*', which I knew, because that's one of the songs that Mam played on our piano – she used to sing as well, so I knew all the words.

I sang like Mam did. But everybody in the altos next to me was singing a different tune, with lower notes. Mam must have been a soprano singer. I tried to sing like the altos, but I couldn't get Mam's tune out of my head and I kept bursting out with her high notes. I knew I should be singing something different, but the tune I had known just kept coming out of my mouth. Mr Jackson kept looking at me and frowning.

In the end, I decided to sing the soprano tune but just a bit lower, so as not to attract attention. Sometimes I went too low and it came out like a grunt, then Mr Jackson shouted, "Who is the growler?"

We had to keep on singing while he came round listening. What could I do?

I went back to my usual soprano only lower. Disaster struck and he got me out in front of everybody.

"It's you!"

What could I say? I decided to say nothing. I didn't go to choir again. It was a mistake to go to choir. I will never be a good singer like Mam.

"We all make mistakes," said Mam. And I knew that was true, because one of our teachers made another mistake. I had moved on to Mr Best's class. He taught us history and was a very big person. He was also very strict and never smiled. We weren't allowed to speak a word in class and when we were sitting waiting for him, we had to sit in silence and put our hands on our head. You would think that he was too perfect to ever make a mistake, but he did. He was teaching us about the Armada. As part of the lessons we had to learn the poem called The Armada by Lord Macaulay.

'Night sank upon the dusky beach...' I liked it when the Spanish were coming to attack, and we lit bonfires all along the coast as a warning. Once one town saw the fire, it lit its own and so on, until here in Yorkshire we knew of an attack. It was a good way of letting everybody know instead of the telephone, which they did not have in those days.

'And saw o'er hanging Richmond Hill...'

"We are going to Richmond," said Mr Best. Everybody, except Mr Best, was very excited, and we missed a day at school. A coach came to pick us up. We had packed lunches (mine were egg sandwiches) and we had to take a camera – I didn't have one, but I borrowed our Katy's which had belonged to Grandma.

"What use have I for photographs, now?" said Grandma with her sour face. It was a very old camera with a black concertina on the front. It let the light in, but I loved borrowing it. It felt important to have a camera even though I knew the photos would be white with light on one side.

We had to wear our school uniform and, as it was an eight o'clock start, Dad had to take me in our van. He wasn't pleased as he had only just finished milking and hadn't had time for breakfast. He dropped me outside Ripsea school and went rushing off to get on with his farm work. I walked up the drive and got our special bus. After a head count, off we chugged, with our form teacher, to Richmond in North Yorkshire. It took us about three hours to get there, just in time to eat our packed lunches. Mr Best stood like a statue, at the front of the bus and watched us all get off.

The bus drove away while we all listened to what Mr Best had to say.

"We are outside Britain's oldest Georgian theatre. I have arranged for us to have a look inside."

We stood on a little path near a road and looked at grey stones which made a sort of barn-like building. A man came along with a key and opened the old creaking door. I looked down at the stage and rows of broken wooden seats. There was an absolutely ancient gold curtain at the front. It was a bit torn.

"This theatre is 170 years old," said Mr Best.

"Just think," I said to Sandra, "people acted, all those years ago, on that little stage." I kept thinking about the actors. And I thought about the people sitting in those seats and how they must have clapped at the shows.

Our family didn't go to the theatre. They hadn't got the time, what with all the work needed to be done on the farm. But I went to a sort of theatre, in Ringam village hall, last year. Veronica told me about it. She was a bit of a show-off and always got good marks at school. Her mam, Mrs White, kept going to our school to ask about Veronica's progress. She wasn't very popular, but I was pleased to know Veronica this time, because she told me about the theatre group she belonged to, and she sold me a ticket for the next show.

"What do you want to go there for?" asked Mam when I wanted money for the ticket. She sounded cross, but she gave me the money all the same.

I loved it. They had put up a wooden stage and there were red curtains across. When they opened with a swish, I watched in amazement. There were singers, dancers and story tellers. Veronica did a ballet dance, and I even liked that. I stared and listened all the way through. I felt that I was in a magical world and not in our little old village hall.

"You sat with your gob open," said Veronica, the next day at school. I was surprised she said 'gob', I thought she was too posh for that.

Then a voice woke me from my thoughts.

"When we have raised enough money, we are going to repair it all, and put on shows again," said the man with the key.

Then that was that, really. Mr Best said he would meet us, in an hour, at the Kings Head Hotel, then off he went. I was with Sandra and we didn't know what to do. Then I remembered that I hadn't taken any photos. So, I took one of the Georgian theatre. There were only three photos left to take. I thought I had better not use up all Katy's film and so I didn't take any more snaps. I didn't know what to take anyway.

Me and Sandra were so scared that we asked the way to the King's Head Hotel straight away. "It is on the marketplace," said a friendly woman. "You can't miss it."

Well, we did miss it, quite a few times. We went back to the theatre and started again. I knew the theatre was on Victoria Street because that was my name, so I had easily remembered it. We followed her instructions again and then found where we should be. We stood outside the King's Head and waited. It started to rain.

I began to sing Perry Como's song about a falling star and Sandra joined in. It helped us not to feel so lonely, but some people stared at us. And some went onto the road to pass us by. Perhaps they knew I was a 'growler'.

Then after a bit, some of the other school kids came back. They were full of excitement telling where they had been. They had been to the castle and round the shops. Some had been to the friary and had a run round the gardens. I wish we had done that, but we were too scared.

The bus came and we got on and went back to school. We had to get our satchels and then catch a late bus home.

It was only when I was in bed that night that I wandered what our trip had to do with the Armada and Lord Macaulay.

I found out in the morning at school.

"We went to the Richmond in the North not the Richmond in the South," said Mr Best. We had gone to the wrong Richmond. Our Richmond was not the one in the poem –

Richmond Hill was down south. Our 'no-nonsense' teacher had made a mistake.

Mam

I wish she had not tried to join the choir, she isn't a good singer. The school has not helped her with that. She's lucky to be going on school trips, though, it's a good opportunity. We never had any – we never went anywhere. What a shame they went to the wrong Richmond.

Never mind. We all make mistakes.

And the war was a mistake surely? Herb didn't agree. He followed the action, on the wireless, but I did not. I had enough to do looking after my family and Ivy and the boy.

I was tired of it all. I bargained with God.

"Please God stop your people fighting, I will never grumble again if you keep us all safe." But the war did not stop, and it was hard to see God's purpose in all this. Everybody in the world seemed to be fighting. Herb used to follow it on the wireless every day at six in the morning before we went to do the milking.

"I don't know how you can listen to all that fighting," I said to Herb one morning. "I am tired of it all."

"It's important to know how we are getting on – you'd sit up and listen if we were invaded. You'd have to."

"But it's just one battle after another, where will that get us?"

"Mebbie you'd listen if your brother or sister were in danger."

"That's not fair."

"No, it's not, sorry love. Listen."

Churchill was on the radio giving us all strength and hope.

It was then that Herb decided it was time to learn to drive. Sid had bought a little second-hand car for them both. Sid loved messing about with the engine and keeping it all in working order. I do not know how he knew what to do, but he did.

"It's time you could drive, I'll give you a lesson," shouted Sid from the front seat. He had driven us for a rare shopping trip in Ringam.

"If you like," answered Herb but I could tell he wasn't keen, and I was sure that the lesson would not be when they got back, because Herb would want to check on the animals as soon as he could. I was right.

Then one day Sid came into our house, "How's tricks? It's time for your driving lesson, I think."

Herb agreed, at last, and Sid did give Herb his lesson in driving. I sat on the old stone which they used to stand on to mount a horse. I heard Sid talk to Herb, then he cranked the car up at the front, and they were off leaping and juddering down the lane. They arrived back a little smoother, and Herb put the hand-brake on and that was it. Herb could drive. I sat beside him and off we went down the lane. The gears made such a noise when he changed up, they grated and shook, but we were still moving forwards.

I began to think that he did not know how to stop. We drove over the railway line and on past field after field, we seemed to go on for ever. Then, at last, a farmyard came into view. Herb crashed down the gears and did a big swoop and we were facing the other way, so we went back up the road and over the railway line and into our yard. We ended in a shuddering stop.

"I'll take you on another trip tomorrow, if you like."

"That would be lovely," I answered, but I felt a bit unsure.

"How did you get on?" shouted Sid.

"Alright, I think, but you say I have to keep my foot on the accelerator all the time?"

"Yes, or else you wouldn't go forwards."

"What if my foot gets tired?"

"That would just be bad luck. You can't use your left foot because you need that for the clutch."

"So, the only change for my right foot is when I brake?"

"That's right."

"I might get cramp."

"That's your look out. Can you turn the engine off now? I'm going to have a look at it – I can hear a bit of a rattle."

Sid always had his head in the engine compartment with his spanners, screwdrivers and grease.

But Herb was a driver! He didn't have to take the Competency Test because the war was on.

"Go and get your licence," I urged when he had been driving for a year or so. And one day he drove to Ringam Offices and got a little red book, which was his licence. It was all stamped and official. I was so proud of him.

I suppose my third baby was a mistake, but I will never tell anybody that. I always thought that it's up to the man, but my babies just kept coming along, even in the war. It can't be right that babies are born into a war.

As it happened my third baby came at the end of the war, on the very day Churchill announced that we had victory in Europe. It was another girl. I had three little girls; Katy was already at school. On the wireless Churchill said that the war in Europe was over.

"Never has there been a greater day than this."

There was cheering and shouting. And so, life settled down to a peaceful routine.

That is until my little baby was suddenly very poorly. It was the teething powder I had put on her gums. She was allergic to it, but I didn't know, did I? It wasn't my fault was it? I questioned myself over and over again. I did my very best for her for months. Was it going to be like Grandma's story all over again? I asked myself. Was I going to lose this daughter? Please God, don't let it all happen to me.

I was spared, and my little baby did not die. She slowly began to gain some strength. I thanked God. We tried to put the whole thing out of our minds.

I will never tell the girls what we went through. I want them to benefit from what we all fought for and not be bogged down by it. We are over it all, and our three girls are growing up and building lives of their own. Things will keep on getting better now.

Everything happened so fast, just like when the war began, but in reverse.

Ivy and her boy went back to start life again in Hull – their house had not been bombed, after all. The soldiers at Grandma's left with their guns. One of the land girls went back home, but of course Vera stayed with her new husband, Sid, and her little boy, Terry. They all lived with Grandma next door.

Electricity poles were put up, all the way down our lane and wires were strung between them, and then telephone wires were fastened on as well. Now we had electricity, everything could be lit up. We had outside lights, inside lights and lights in the calving sheds and our cows were milked by our new Alfa Laval system, with a standby generator. Nothing had to stand in the way of our cows being milked.

We had everything, but I wanted to leave.

When I had my third little girl, I began thinking that we must go. But Sid and Herb would not hear of it.

"Grandma says it would kill her," whispered Sid.

"You can understand it – she has lost four children and could not bear to lose another," said Herb.

"It would be a mistake to go," said Sid.

"Look at all we have here," said Herb.

So, I stopped nagging, for now, I couldn't bear it if I made a mistake and it hurt Grandma and Herb and Sid. But I could not help thinking about it as the years went by.

Chapter 12

Moving on

Me

One day, I heard from our Gwendy that we were moving, after all. We were moving to a house in Sunkstead, which was the village next to ours on the Hull road. Dad and Uncle Sid had bought a new farm. Its fields joined up with our land at Gum, and we were going to leave our old house, at Gum, and go to live in another farmhouse. I had only ever lived in one house and I didn't know what it would be like to move.

Something else was moving as well, and that was the 'BBCs'. One day I looked out of my bedroom window and I could see the vegetable garden, then our fields and a strip of trees then away towards Sunkstead and Hull. But something was different. You see, in one of the fields just beyond ours, there had always been the BBCs. They were so tall they reached into the sky and on the top of each one was a red light. Mam said that they sent messages in the war and that bombs had been dropped to try and destroy them. Well, now we destroyed them ourselves because we didn't need them any more, now we were not at war.

Uncle Tom was part of the team that helped to take them down. He blamed this job for his constipation because he said that there was no toilet at the top. Well, of course there wouldn't be, how could there be? He climbed a ladder that went straight to the top, every morning, and then started undoing nuts and bolts.

"Once you were there you had to stay up for the morning. It took so long to climb the ladder that it wasn't worth coming down. You had to hold everything in, till dinner time," laughed

Uncle Tom. And so, his constipation got worse, while the masts gradually got shorter and shorter until they had gone altogether.

"I trained myself to go only once a week, on a Sunday," he told me. His bowels have been altered and now our view from my window towards Sunkstead was changed as well.

Sunkstead was where Brenda, my primary school friend lived. When I used to go to her farm all I ever wanted, was to live near her, so we could play all day. But now we were older and in different classes and usually only saw each other on the bus, things were changing fast. One thing that didn't change though, was my school — I still had to go to the same school, which turned out to be good news really. I had got a bit better at French and was doing alright in my other subjects.

When we moved Uncle Sid and Aunty Vera would stay with their family to look after things at their end at Gum. They would look after Grandma as well. We would look after things at the Sunkstead end.

There was a lot of planning first. Animals had to be moved and the new cow house and dairy made ready. Mam and Dad started travelling to our new farm to do the milking and Mam started some packing of our clothes. They took things in our van bit by bit. They left our big kitchen table, where we had all had our breakfasts, dinners and teas. It was where we had played table tennis, where Mam had ironed and where I had done my homework. But it was too big for our new house. They left our old carved wardrobes and our mahogany dresser and book shelves which held big blocks of salt, waiting to be rubbed into our hanging hams. They left the horse hair chairs, near the fire, and all our big furniture which had probably been there since the house was built.

On the last day they took our beds. Then that night we moved ourselves. I crouched in the back of our van, clinging on to Katy's kidney-shaped table, with a slippery glass top. She didn't want it any more, even though Mam had made a pink curtain and a frill to go round it. Mam said that it was too good to leave behind.

But I had to leave my den behind, I had worked on it for a long time. I left my tree house behind as well; you could climb the tree and sit in it and look out and see the trains chugging to Ripsea. You could see all our fields spread out in front of you.

I left our woods, our orchard and our deadly drain. I left my cousins Terry, Stewy and Bonny with little Bobby. It seemed as if I was leaving my childhood behind and I did not think I wanted to do that. I felt a bit frightened, but like Uncle Tom, I held everything in, in a different way, of course.

Then, just when I thought we would settle into our new house, Gwendy left. All of a sudden, she went nursing in Beverley and we couldn't talk together at night. I was on my own, so there was nothing to do but read. Gwendy's new bedroom was empty, now she had gone. And our Katy had a house of her own, now she was married, so she didn't need a bedroom here. Everything was so different.

But the whispering didn't stop – and this time it went on just under my bedroom where the floorboards were loose and wood-wormed. Uncle Sid used to come some nights when my Dad was milking, and Mam was carrying the buckets of milk to the dairy. Suddenly, the car was outside, and Mam rushed in and there it was again –

"Wsss, wsss, wsss."

It was like a woodworm sawing its little round holes in the wood. There was silence for a minute, then it all started again only louder and stronger.

"Wsss, wsss, wssss."

As I lay on my bed upstairs, I wished that I could be that woodworm and bore right through to see what was going on underneath my feet. Was it a sign that something else was going to happen? How could it be when we had already moved to a new house?

Well, I hadn't got time to think any more about that because for one thing, I had to get on with my homework.

Back at school the next day in my science class, Mr Boyes, our science teacher, was throwing sweets at us. We had just finished our exams and we were waiting nervously for the results. When he hit you with a sweet, he called a number.

"One," he shouted when he hit me. I was just trying to think what he was doing, and what it was all about, when a messenger came from Mr Sparrow. Mr Sparrow wanted to see me.

Me to go to Mr Sparrow? What had I done wrong? Maybe he was going to tell me off for letting him think that I was called Virginia, when I was serving the teachers. Whatever it was, I was scared. I walked down that carpeted corridor and gently knocked on his door.

"Come in."

This time I didn't go round to his side of the desk, I stood in the middle of his big room and looked down at the whirly leaves on his red carpet.

"I think that it would be a good idea for you to take sciences for you GCEs."

I looked up then. And saw his bald head with black hair all around the sides. I saw his black rimmed glasses and his big black cloak.

I was going to choose art and history and religious education. I liked those subjects. I was quite good at painting and learning about things in the past. Going to chapel and Sunday school had taught me a lot about the Bible.

"I would like you to take physics, chemistry and biology." Then he looked up and smiled a flat smile.

"Well that's all for now, off you go to get on with your work."

I turned and left in a hurry.

Back in Mrs Boyes class, Sandra told me what the numbers with the sweets meant.

If he shouted 'One' then you were first in the exam, 'two' and you were second and so on. So... I was 'one' and I was first – top marks in a science exam.

I was going to be a scientist. At home, I decided that I had better start looking the part. I pulled my hair back, like Mam had started to do with hers. I pulled it all back from my face and clipped it into a roll using hair grips.

Then I needed a desk. The only table in my room was Katy's glass kidney table that she didn't need any more. It had been made to fit in a corner near her bed and was for her make-up. But it didn't fit well here and was a bit wobbly now. The curtains didn't meet, and however hard I pulled, I could not move them. It was the best I could do. I put my pen on top and a pencil and a ruler and rubber. I put my leather satchel underneath on the floor. And I dragged the little bedroom chair up. Now I was ready to begin, but then Mam called, and it was tea time. I ran downstairs.

Nobody said anything about my hair. Nobody noticed. I didn't really think that Dad would notice, but I did think Mam would say 'How nice you look with your hair up, just like mine.' But she didn't and so after tea I went back upstairs to sit at my desk and took my hair grips out.

I could hear the gentle hum of her new electric sewing machine. Her treadle Singer machine had been dumped and she had this new one with a grey plastic cover with red edging. It didn't rattle and Mam didn't have to pedal her feet. She switched it on and away it hummed smoothly.

I was sad about the old machine. I loved its big wheel and the brown cord round it, which was connected to the pedal. I loved the little lever which took the cord away from the machinery, so when Mam was not using it, you couldn't accidentally make it stitch. I used to dust it carefully with a soft cloth in between all the spokes and gently over the gold lettering and gears. There were little wooden drawers on each side to hold the scissors and needles and a long tilting compartment to hold the cottons. When we weren't using it, which wasn't very often, you could press a catch and hide the sewing arm underneath. Then you could fold the top over so that it all just looked like a side table. Mam used to put her embroidery samples on it, and you could admire them as you went past.

With the new machine, I couldn't see any of the workings as they were all cased up in plastic. It sat on our table and didn't fold away, you just put the grey cover on. It had a red handle so you could lift it down and put it in a cupboard out of sight. Mam seemed to like it and she said it was progress, and that had to be a good thing.

"Life is moving on and we have to move with it," said Mam. Things change and that is progress.

Then, when I was in bed, in my new bedroom, I heard the church clock strike 'Ding, dong'. I scrambled up and looked out of the window – the blue clock face was lit up. I squinted to focus. I wasn't as good at seeing things in the distance as I used to be.

At Gum we never had any clocks – we didn't need them, we got up when Mam said and went to bed when she said. That was all there was really – when we were hungry, we came in for dinner or tea. We knew time was passing when winter changed to spring and spring changed to summer then autumn. We knew how much daylight we had left by where the sun was in the sky. Now, we had made progress and we would know what time it was by the ring of the church clock.

'Ding dong, ding dong,' that was half past ten. I lay down trying to get to sleep and suddenly I was frightened. What if I didn't sleep all night? I would lay awake hearing the clock ring out saying that I should be asleep. At Gum, I just got into bed and I fell asleep without thinking about it. Now, in my new bedroom, I knew every quarter of an hour that I was still awake.

'Ding dong, ding dong, ding dong,' that was quarter to eleven. The last 'Ding dong' sounded in a different tune from the first, as it laughed at me through the window. I gave in and lay awake for the eleven 'boings' on the hour. Then I listened, stiff and tense all through to twelve midnight as the ding dongs were repeated. Then the boings crunched through my brain again and trapped me in a nightmare.

Mam woke me up in time to get ready for school.

"Get a move on" she shouted. "You are late."

Everything, it seemed, was getting a move on and making progress. Everybody in our class has a bust except me – you couldn't help but notice. Brenda was well developed, and she was looking at boys and fancying them. I really wanted to make dens and play in our fields with the kids next door and our Gwendy. But Gwendy was older, and Mam said that she was developing. In the end she developed so quickly that she upped and left home to get a job. Once I asked Mam why I hadn't developed

"Give it time – you will," she said, and I did. I didn't like it, but it happened all the same.

I tried on a bra that our Gwendy had left behind but it was too big for me and I looked down at the crumpled grey roses and quickly buttoned up my school blouse to hide it. I said nothing while my body did what it was always going to do. It got a move on and that was progress. Maybe that's what Mam and Uncle Sid were whispering about.

But it turned out that I wasn't the big news after all. Our Katy came home one day with her husband with news that the whispering must have told.

She was going to have a baby – our Katy going to have a baby.

Life was moving on faster than I thought it would.

Mam

I got anxious once more about our future. I began to get restless again. I nagged him for the umpteenth time (although I knew I shouldn't).

"Herb," I said, "We have three girls and next door have three boys. They will grow up and have the farm. What will our girls have?"

"They'll be alright," he always said. "There'll be plenty for us all." He thought that hard work would solve everything, but I was beginning to doubt.

"The girls will get married and move away and have their own children," he said.

"But what about us two?" I always asked. He never answered; he just worked all hours. That's all he ever wanted. He trusted that the future would be alright. He was too trusting. We had to make the future ourselves, I thought.

"Why don't we sell up?"

"How can we?"

"Well, we could just sell our half of the farm to Sid and then buy something nice for ourselves."

"It's not as easy as that. You know it would kill Grandma to lose another child."

"But she wouldn't be losing you. We could visit every week or so."

"It's not the same. How can I do that to Mother when she has gone through so much?"

And so, we did nothing except work. I was getting tired and time was getting on. I could feel it ticking away in my little finger on my left hand.

But miraculously, somebody was selling up. There was a farm, called Village Farm, for sale in the next village and the land adjoins ours. We were in a position to buy it jointly, and so Sid and Herb did. We all set to work.

We got the builders in first to make the house ready for living in. It was much smaller – a beamed cottage in the village of Sunkstead. I was going to have a kitchen – a real kitchen not an old cold wash house. I have chosen yellow for the colour scheme. Best of all I am to have a twin tub washer and a new cooker.

"Choose what you want," said Herb then added, true to form, "within reason." The washer and cooker were bought – ordered from Ringam but the money was being spent too fast.

Vera and Grandma had a new cooker and washer, as well, to make it fair.

I felt that I had to make some savings. So, I went to the saleroom in Hull to buy a second-hand kitchen cabinet with a drop-down work surface. I painted it yellow and white. I could hardly wait to go.

"We're ready to move the herd," said Herb, one day. The cows were coming with us and the new milking parlour and dairy were ready.

"How will we do that?"

"We'll walk them on our main road."

So that's what we did. Our fine tubercular tested herd was walked to their new modern quarters. Herb emphasised it was a TT herd. We always had to say that, we had to teach the girls to say that. I expect it was because of his sisters dying of tuberculosis. We had to be sure our milk was disease free. Mind you, they have better drugs now.

I was in front and Herb was at the back in our van, with Sid walking along side.

"You have to carry something white at the front," said Sid, "to warn any vehicles." So, there I was carrying an old shirt. I waved it once or twice, when I saw a truck. It was a long trek because the cows wanted to eat grass on the way, or cross the road and Sid had to shout,

"Whoa, get on there."

Our black and white rumbling mass walked the road in a slow, wavy line – a mile and a half of it and then they were safely at their new home in Village Farm.

I have been sewing non-stop at night making curtains with pelmets for the windows. And during the day I went to the saleroom again and again to buy furniture which I could sand down and polish. I loved it.

And then we were on our last journey from Gum to Sunkstead, in our van with my embroidery in my grey case on my knee. Vi was in the back of the van pulling her coat against the cold, she is such a scrap of a thing. Our Gwendy had suddenly decided to go nursing in Beverley, and so my new life was ready to begin.

I am so happy. Two of my daughters are nurses. What better profession? I am so proud of them and so happy that they are making their way in life, free to make choices of their own in this new modern world.

The phone was ringing. It was on our own phone, no rushing to Grandma's next door to take a message – our Katy's baby had been born in Hull hospital and it's a boy!

"It's better than I have done," said Herb.

I know that he meant it was better than I had done as well – and I felt bad because I hadn't given him a boy. It made me tremble to think of our Katy having a baby boy. I had not done that, and I had failed Herb. Maybe it wasn't my fault, but it felt like it.

Sid called to see us, he always dressed smartly, not like Herb. I had to badger Herb into changing out of his farm clothes when we were going out and, even if he was going shopping at Ringam, he wouldn't change.

Sid was different, what with him driving tractors and then getting changed in the afternoon to do the paperwork. When he called in at Sunkstead, he was going into Hull on business, so he had his best outfit on.

He waltzed in through our front door.

"How's tricks?"

"Come and see my kitchen," I said. I was proud of that new kitchen with bright yellow linoleum flooring. My tall kitchen cabinet with a drop-down shelf where I rolled my pastry was the latest thing for women to have.

"You don't look very well," he whispered.

"It's just the yellow reflection," I whispered back. My little finger on my left hand started to twitch – tick, tick it went.

'Time is ticking on,' it was saying. I held it with my right hand to steady it. Then, Sid was off, he revved up our new

Zephyr car and swooped away. Herb always liked driving the van, even though the car was shared.

But I had plenty of other things to think about now, I lived in a village where there was a lot going on. It was all so easy after living down that lane at Gum. I started going to sewing classes at Sunkstead (as much for the company as anything else) and I went to the Women's Institute here and to the chapel which is just down the road. They asked me to play the organ sometimes and I loved that.

I had done all these things before, but I had to get a bus, or ask Herb to drive me there. Now, I was free to do what I wanted as long as I had finished my work on the farm and in the house.

I still visited Ringam, though, to see my sister and brothers, every now and again. I liked to make sure they were well, even though they were all grown up now.

I was enjoying this new life. I decided to put my hair up in a chignon. Poor little Vi tried to put her thin strands of hair up. She looks better with it down, but I didn't like to say.

"I need a new sewing machine," I told Herb one day not long after we moved. "The treadle is so old, I have had it since we married. I need an up-to-date model."

"We'll have to see how things go this year; you can't be too careful." That was just like Herb, always careful, always adding up the pros and cons.

Then, at the end of the financial year, I got my new sewing machine, at last. Herb had said there was nothing wrong with my old one, but I had seen the new one in the sewing shop in Hull and I just couldn't seem to get it out of my mind. I kept begging him and, in the end, he gave in and handed me the money for the new one, I was so grateful.

And here it is, my brand-new sewing machine I will be able to get my sewing done in half the time, I thought. Things were looking up for me. New house, new sewing machine and new time for myself at home. What with Katy and Gwendy gone, and little Vi who will be away soon, I will have even more time than ever for my sewing and embroidery. I might even join more things here in Sunkstead.

I love my neat modern kitchen. The new cooker is so easy to use. It seems to heat up in an instant and has four plates on the top with a big oven underneath. I love cooking with it especially breakfast. But there's just a bit of a worry at the back of my mind and I notice it especially today when I fry the bacon. I still can't smell – even when I burn it slightly it still has no smell to me. Of course, it's not a new thing. I have noticed it before and made excuses – like having a cold. I have not taken it too seriously, but today it hits me.

I have no sense of smell.

I rush to find the Dettol bottle under the sink. I still remember what Dettol smells like, and I take the cap off and put my nose to the rim. Nothing. I wave it about under my nose and sniff. Nothing. How can that be? What's gone wrong? I try my old perfume bottle – 'Ashes of Violets' – at my dressing table upstairs. Nothing. I dash into the fold yard, where the cows are waiting to go out into the field after milking. I know their warm soft smell and the stink of their mess on the straw.

"Herb, I can't smell anything."

"We know that. You haven't been able to smell for ages."

"But today it seems worse. I have been able to smell things on and off, but today there's nothing"

"Mebbie it'll come back. All of a sudden, when you aren't thinking about it, you'll get it back. Then you might wish you hadn't, if you are in this yard!" He smiled gently and went off to let the cows into our field.

But it did not come back, and I started to really miss it. Where has it gone? I had five senses and now I have lost one. So, there are only four left. Good heavens, I thought of Herb's sisters dying, first one going and then another. Surely, I won't lose my sight and hearing or my taste and feeling? It does not bear thinking about.

Maybe Herb is right, and it will come back one day. His four sisters didn't come back though, I keep remembering that.

The BBCs
By the author (age 13)

Chapter 13

Half child half adult

Me

After the holiday I am back at school. Mam made my school uniform again, and I wished again, that I could have new clothes from the school outfitter shop, like everybody else.

"Make the skirt tighter," I bossed as strongly as I dared. Nowadays, I wanted to look 'with it' like Brenda and the others. I didn't want to look frumpy.

"It's not tight enough. Everybody wears them tight nowadays, Mam." She took the sides in a bit, but I still would have liked it skin-tight. It looked too big. As for the length, it was too long as usual, but I wasn't too worried about that. When I set off to school, and I was at the bus stop, I hitched the skirt up and rolled the waistband. I reckoned I could lift the hem about two inches like this. I did it every day, I didn't want my skirt below my knees. Mind you, I had to look out for Mademoiselle at school, she was the person who searched out girls with skirts that were too short. If I saw her, I quickly unrolled my waistband and I was never caught. But my friend Brenda was once.

"Kneel down, Brenda," commanded Mademoiselle. And Brenda had to kneel down, there and then in the corridor in front of us all, and her skirt hem had to touch the floor – which it didn't.

"Stand up, Brenda, and let us see what the problem is," said Mademoiselle. Brenda had to stand there, while her waistband was unrolled from the belt. Her skirt fell to below her knees. She had to stand in front of us all looking a real mess, with a drooping long skirt, while Mademoiselle gave her a lecture.

Brenda wasn't bothered though. When we got round the corner, she just rolled her waistband and her skirt was short again.

One thing that is good about our new village, Sunkstead, is that there is a shop. It is just down the path from our house. About two minutes' walk. I liked this because I could dash there when I had forgotten something that I really needed. I never had much money, though – I had to rely on Mam to give me a bit.

Mrs March runs the shop. She is very old and wears a wrap-over flowery pinny like Grandma. The shop is brown and shabby, but it has a big bay window that goes round two sides so you can see what you want to buy.

Mind you, if you wanted to buy something for 'down below', you couldn't see it easily, because all that sort of thing was wrapped in brown paper. You didn't get to see it before you got it home. Today I want a comb, I really wanted to do something about my hair. How could I look good when my hair looked like this? Mam always cut it and after she had finished it always looked old fashioned and flat.

We had a bus shelter at our bus stop in Sunkstead and, on a school day, Brenda was there – oh how I loved her hair. She had kiss curls at the side, and it swept straight back from the front. Brian was there – he was older than me and had a job in a sweet shop in Ripsea. He got a bit of work even in the winter because he was so good at selling. That's why he had enough money for cigarettes, and I could see the smoke billowing out of the shelter door as I walked up. You weren't supposed to smoke on your way to school. He went upstairs on the bus after stubbing out his fag and Brenda and I went downstairs.

When I got home that night there was bad news for me.

"You have to have your passages cleaned out," said Mam. Is that what she had been whispering about with Uncle Sid?

Which passages? What was she talking about? She should know I am studying biology and know a good lot about the human body. I suppose they are checking my lungs and the bronchioles. No good talking to Mam about it though – she wouldn't understand the terms I use. I realise now that the fortune teller was wrong. I am nothing like my mam and I have given up trying to be like her, once and for all.

We had a new doctor, now we had moved. He was called Doctor Newby and he had dark hair and was good looking and young. Old Doctor Moon was still at Ringam but now he had this partner called Doctor Newby.

Our new doctor's surgery was in the next village towards Hull, in Mudlington. You had to go to his house, just like when you went to see Doctor Moon in his massive mansion with its sweeping gravel drive. But the new doctor's house was much smaller and now we had to go up a path, down the side of his house and into a little lean-to room with wooden chairs all round.

It was always full, and you had to wait. Mrs Newby was the person in charge at a table, and once, when I was waiting with Mam, the phone went. You could hear it, but it wasn't on Mrs Newby's table, it was in the main house. There was no door to the main house inside, so Mrs Newby went rushing off to answer it and came back to talk to Doctor Newby. He then dashed off and we were all just left sitting there.

"Doctor has had to go out on an emergency," she announced. "I would advise you to go home and come back another day."

We sat there, we didn't go and neither did anyone else. Then after two hours, Doctor Newby came back and carried on with seeing everybody. He sounded my chest and tapped my rib cage and asked me to breathe in and out. I thought that was that but of course it wasn't – it never is with doctors. My passages needed attention. And now I had to go into hospital. What on earth am I going to do about my O level exams?

I didn't tell anybody. I didn't want to talk about it. It would be awful, and I did not want people messing about with my body, either. What if there is a scar? How would I get a boyfriend if I was disfigured?

Anyway, it wasn't up to me. Mam put my nighty in her grey embroidery case and got Dad to take us to Hull infirmary. I packed my little 'bucket' bag with an old lipstick of Mam's, squeezed up with my physics notes from school, and off we went.

The hospital was a really old building with big pillars in front and an old statue of a man outside with a piece of paper. It was all like something out of a bad dream.

We went to Reception and Mam asked for my ward. I didn't speak. Dad looked straight ahead, and he didn't speak either.

My ward was a ward for women. Well of course it would be, but somehow, I expected to be on the children's ward, even though I was certainly not a child. But a surgical ward for women was not what I expected.

"Here we are, my dear," said the nurse clip-clipping along the old corridor.

"We thought you'd be happier in this three-bed bay with two others, as you are so young, dear."

She talked in a high voice, as if she was talking to a child. I plonked down on the bed. The paint-peeling sash window behind me was draughty and I pulled my cardi round me.

"Oh! Don't let matron see you sitting on your bed, my dear, it is not hygienic you know. Now, when you are ready just pop your nighty on, and get into bed for me."

I got up but didn't speak to her. She pulled some old green curtains round us. What an awful, awful place. The blankets were grey and there was an off-white cover.

I lay there staring at the yellow wall and Mam and Dad left, with my clothes in the grey case.

"Ta-ra," shouted Dad as he sped away to get back to his farm. They both went so fast, it looked as if they couldn't wait to get away.

A woman came in wearing her 'glad rags' – my dad used to call clothes that, when women dressed to impress and have a good time. I can't think that she would be having a good time here. Her poppy red dress showed up every curve and the neckline was very low 'it left nothing to the imagination,' as my mam would say. She got into bed in a thin orange flimsy nighty with a little burn hole in. Then she got out again and came to see me.

"Hello, I'm Shirley. I'm glad we are in this little ward. It's cosier don't you think?"

She sat on my bed and kicked her red slippers off and tucked her feet under my off-white bedspread. She smiled at me, shrugging her shoulders in a fun way. I didn't know what to do. So I just lay there without moving.

"What are you having done, love?"

"My tubes cleaned," I muttered.

"Oh, so am I, that's smashing, isn't it?"

She slapped my bed, in another fun sort of way.

"God, I wish I could have a fag. Do y'think they'll let me have one before the operation?"

How would I know? I shrugged and stared at her.

"Well I'm off to find out." She pushed into her velvet slippers and grabbed her red handbag and went. You could see through her nighty.

Another woman came in.

"Hello love, I'm Betty, I'm just going to get into me nighty and then I'm coming over to give you a hug."

She gave me a big bear hug and pulled me to her big bosoms. She nearly smothered me.

"There that's better, isn't it?" She pushed back and smiled. Her soft black curls looked like a halo round her face, if you can have a black halo. She smiled at me all the time, as if I was her very best friend. As if I was her only true friend. I felt her candlewick dressing gown tender and feathery against my cheeks. I was safe here, hidden away in her folds. I wanted to stay there for ever, folded in her warm pink arms and soft breasts.

She stroked my hair. "Nice hair, dear. I wish mine was as smooth." Who on earth would want hair like mine if they had bubbly curls like hers?

Shirley came back in a cloud of smoke. She stubbed her cigarette out in the sink.

"That's better, thank God for a fag. How are you, love?" I didn't have time to answer because a nurse came in to check our temperatures and things. Curtains were pulled round us in turn. Then –

"Supper, everybody. Come along. Last meal before your ops." Betty linked arms with me and off we went to a long trestle table in the middle of a big ward. I didn't want anything to eat. Then it was back to bed and lights out.

Betty and Shirley talked into the night. They talked about 'down below'.

"I've got fibroids, so they are going to clear them, I've been having pain at my time of the month. I only hope they can help me."

"They don't know what's wrong with me, I can't get pregnant, I don't get my little friend every month, so they are clearing my tubes just in case they are blocked. Hubby wants a son and heir. So, I go through all this. Men eh?"

"Have you brought any bunnies?"

"Yes, I don't suppose they give you any here and we could bleed after the op."

"Oh, Gawd, I didn't bring any, can I lend yours?"

The girls in my class called them 'bunnies' but Mam always said 'STs' in a sort of whisper. Nobody dared to mention sanitary towels.

I carried on listening to Shirley and Betty, then suddenly wondered – was I having a 'down below' operation after all? Would Shirley lend me some bunnies?

I didn't have to wonder long. Next morning, we had to get into green starch-stiff gowns with a split at the back and then put hats on, like my shower cap at school.

"Gawd," laughed Shirley. "I hope I don't get taken short and have to walk to the lav. You'd see all I've got." I didn't like to say I had already seen it through her thin nighty.

"You alright, my love?" asked Betty shouting across the aisle to me. I didn't have time to answer before I was wheeled off on a trolley to the theatre. I knew what this was all about from when I had my tonsils out, when I was little. And I knew it wasn't a theatre like the Georgian theatre in Richmond, or even the village hall make-shift theatre where Veronica had performed. This was a theatre where they did operations on your body.

I wasn't being put to sleep this time, like I had been with my tonsil operation. Some drops were put in my nose – it wasn't down below then – and some wires went in and then some more instruments and the surgeon pressed, and I could hear crunching in my head. I wished Betty was with me now – hugging me and smiling at me, just as if I was her very own little girl. But nobody was with me, except the surgeon pressing and rinsing. I had to hold a kidney basin to my face as my nose was flooded with water. Blood came out.

When I got back to my little ward. Betty and Shirley weren't there.

They came back much later, and they were very quiet for the rest of the day. We were all in bed and hardly spoke for a few days.

"Shall I wash your hair, love?" That was Shirley. She washed it with her own Drene shampoo. We only used soap at home. She dried it for about an hour with her hands. It was lovely to feel her fingers on my scalp, so tender and tingly.

"You have such soft hair, love, it's gorgeous. I could style it for you." I really liked her touching my head and I wanted to be fashionable and with it, so I let her cut it even shorter than Mam had. When it was nearly dry, she put some pin curlers in. She teased the sides of my hair into kiss curls and then Sellotaped them in place, sticking them to my cheeks. We sat and talked. She showed me her make-up bag and told me about things in there. She showed me her eye shadow, Max Factor crème puff and lots of lipsticks. Mam only had one. When my hair was finally dry, she took the curlers out and ran her hands through again.

"You need lots of lacquer, love, I'll do it." And she sprayed so much I could hardly breathe.

"You look a million dollars, love." I looked in the mirror and saw a different person. I did really look so 'with it', I hadn't known I could look like this. I shook my head, but my hair didn't move. It was just what I wanted.

"I'll give you a makeover, if you want," said Shirley and I couldn't resist. She put coloured cream on my face and plucked my eyebrows, till tears welled up in my eyes, but I wanted it done. She put blue eye shadow on me and lipstick. Wow!

"Be careful," Betty warned but I didn't know what she was talking about. I didn't need her arms round me now. I didn't need her cuddles and her reassuring smiles. I was certainly not a child any more. I am a new person and I like it.

Mam

I hated taking Vi to hospital. I knew that Herb really did not want to go, I had to persuade him to get changed and shaved. We couldn't go on the bus, though, could we? What a thing to take our girl to Hull, to have an operation, on the bus.

"Hurry up," said Herb as soon as he was ready, and we bustled into the car with my little grey case. He wanted to get back to his animals as quickly as he could. "Cows don't look after themselves you know. And there's milking at six." As if I could forget.

Sid and Vera's eldest two boys were growing fast, and Terry, had already left school and was working full time on the farm at Gum. So, everything would be alright without us.

"Don't drive so fast, Herb," I said, as he drove away from the hospital at top speed to get back to his animals.

"We are leaving our little girl behind."

But he drove fast all the same.

"She isn't a little girl any more – she's growing up and they've put her in a grown-up ward with grown-up women."

"They have put her in a gyne ward, though, and that will not be nice." Herb didn't answer, he just drove home.

When she was in hospital, a large envelope arrived with the postmark Ripsea. It was Vi's school report. As she was not at school when they gave them out, they sent it to us. One of us had to sign it, as usual, and then we had to post it back. I had always signed it. Herb never really looked at the girls' school reports.

"Good heavens – look at this, Herb," I said when he came in for a mug of tea.

"Our Vi seems to be a bit of a scholar. Look, really good marks in some subjects."

"Mebbie she takes after me!" he laughed. But it was true, even though he didn't like school and never tried hard to learn, he was good at mental arithmetic and knew how to make a profit at market with his animals. He was quick witted and soon cottoned on to situations. He never really learned about writing though, and he thought reading was lazy.

"You've always got your head stuck in a book," he would say to Vi. "Come and help me with these lambs. Never mind about book learning."

I was good at sewing and embroidery. I was a reasonable singer and I had neat handwriting and I found it easy to play the piano, but I was beginning to realise that, although Vi was not good at the things I did, she might be good at other things.

I signed her report with pride and, strangely, Herb came and put his signature to it as well.

"You hardly ever look at the school reports," I said astonished.

"Well I've started now. Mebbie she'll make a different life for herself."

At Gum, Herb saw to it that we had a lot of good fresh vegetables in the garden. Sometimes, if the cabbages were not ready, I cut fresh nettle tops or dandelion leaves. They are full of minerals I am told. I should have found some to cook today.

"What a stink," said Herb when he came in for dinner. I was cooking a cabbage bought from the Mrs March's Sunkstead shop.

He did not like vegetables that were not fresh. He had a garden here, but he didn't want to grow vegetables any more, he said that he wanted a change. So now he grew flowers instead. He loved the bright colours and the big flower heads. They grew so well, with some as high as the surrounding wall. It was a sight for all to see.

"Good job you can't smell it," he laughed, "but I can, and we'd better throw it away."

When we picked Vi up a few days later, I thought 'Good heavens, she has changed from a child to an adult, almost overnight.' I had the strange feeling that she was a different person altogether. She had a very modern hairstyle and she seemed aloof and distant.

'It will be the operation,' I told myself. 'I am sure she will soon be back to normal.'

Chapter 14

Going forwards and backwards

Me

Sometimes you go forwards and sometimes you go backwards. Now we were at our new house in Sunkstead, we looked out of the window to see brick walls and a corrugated tin shed. This was the village hall and the brick walls were surrounding a garden belonging to the house opposite. When I was at our old farm, we looked on our own garden and then our own fields and away towards Hull.

It was different now, you could see everybody walking on the footpath over the road, or on the footpath next to our house. Sometimes in the morning, if it was a big person walking for the bus on our side, they practically blacked out the light from our tiny window, and it made me jump.

There was a woman, who I watched, always on the opposite side. She used to rush along then, all of a sudden, she stopped and turned round and walked back a bit. I thought, 'She won't catch her bus at this rate.' But she kept going and as long as she went forwards more than she went back, she got to the bus stop.

"She wants to make up her mind," said my dad.

"Do not talk about her like that. She has a nervous disposition. It's just like a tic," said my mam. I suppose she meant that she couldn't help it, like Mr Hellas saying, "with it," at the end of every sentence. I just liked watching her in amazement as she sometimes went forwards and sometimes backwards.

I was going forwards in a big way. I had been good enough in my trial class and had already gone up into the prestigious Scholarship class. Sandra had come as well and some of the others. Mostly I didn't know any of the pupils that had been in the upper class from the start. Our form teacher was Mr Boyes who taught us science and now he was teaching us physics. He was very big and strong looking. He said that he used to teach in a private school for boys, so he wasn't used to girls. He told us to let him know if he was too strict. I thought that no one would dare tell him. But I needn't have worried because, although he made us work hard, he was not frightening at all and was always very kind to me. The only other girl in my physics class was Amy. And she was very serious about working hard. But she always had a smile for me.

I was studying the sciences, but Sandra did something I thought was strange. She said that she wanted to study shorthand and typing. She had the chance to get O levels, but she gave most of them up, and went down to the typing group.

"I've got a better chance of getting a job, if I can type," she said. Life was zooming head-long and so many things were changing.

At my new home I walk on tarmac when I go out of our front door, I used to walk on cobbles and grass or mud, and up our stony lane. Now, I walk on proper tarmacked footpaths.

If I go down our side road and on to the main road and look east, I can just see my old home in the distance. The home in Gum, where I lived for my first years. I can see our wood, like a dark strip of trees with their arms outstretched, as if they are stopping me from going to my old home. I can see where our railway line goes round and over our drain. I can see our tiny distant farmhouse and its comforting red brick, and it looks like smoke is coming out of the chimney. Aunty Vera will have lit the fire and Grandma will be sitting near it.

Sometimes I still long to go back and play with the kids next door and ride our bikes and run up the road. I know I can't though, they aren't there any more they have grown up, like me. I can't go there any more. I have left it all behind.

You can't go forwards and then go backwards, like that woman on the pavement opposite. Even when she tries to go back, something makes her turn round and go forwards again. Forwards to catch the bus and forwards to the rest of her life.

I have to go forwards to school and study. And there is bad news at school. Although I am doing a bit better with my French it's still letting me down, says Mademoiselle. I need to have another language to get anywhere in life. So, I had to have a French pen-friend. It was all arranged, and she was called Murielle. She was in Paris. She had to write to me in English and I had to write to her in French.

At first, I liked reading her letters. They came airmail, in a blue folding envelope with strange stamps. I didn't like answering her letters though. As I have said, I had to write in French, and it was not easy for me to do that.

'Cher Murielle...' I wrote and then I was stuck. One day, Mam came back from Hull with a French/English dictionary. It was a great big tome and must have cost a lot. I wrote my name in ink across the closed pages at the side. But I still didn't know what to write to this Murielle who lived in Paris.

Once, I got a good idea and listed the animals on our farm. All I had to do was look them up in the English section and, as we had quite a lot, it took up a lot of space on the thin blue paper.

When it was Easter, I sent Murielle a 'cadeau' – it was a box of little soaps in different colours all shaped like eggs. Dad was mad at me because they were heavy. I had to ask him for the postage, and it cost a lot.

"Mebbie you should have sent hankies," he said, "it would have been a lot cheaper." She wrote back to me and said, 'Your gift was delicious' – and I thought 'Oh no she has eaten them, and they are soap.' But when I looked up the French for 'delicious' in my dictionary, it said 'delicieux' which can mean 'delightful'. So that was alright then. But it was only alright till I got another letter from her, and I had to write back.

In the end, I hated the blue envelopes coming with Posty. It wasn't even our old Posty on a bike, it was a new Posty walking round with his bag. He didn't even come in or knock on our door to give Mam our letters. We had a letter box in the front door now, and he posted them in there, and it was rusty and creaked when letters were pushed in. Mademoiselle said that my French was rusty.

The good news is that I am old enough to get a job at Ripsea. Brian, at our bus stop, worked at Cathy's Candy. Our Gwendy used to work there at the shop, and so I went to try my luck. Cathy was the name of the owner's little girl, who had died. There was a picture of her in a pink sun hat on the office desk. Her mother's name was Amelia, but everybody called her Mealy. I stood there staring at the photo of that little girl, while Mealy asked me a few questions – she knew who I was, and she knew my family, so there wasn't much to ask.

I got the job. Starting straight away. I wasn't ready to start straight away. But she put a pinny on me and there I was selling ice cream and ice lollies. I had to wear a hat as well – it was like a white trilby hat with a band round that said, 'Cathy's Candy'.

The hat was too big for me and I took it off when meany Mealy wasn't there. I wasn't much good at selling, everybody went to buy from Brian. He was in the class above me, his hat fitted. He wore it at an angle and Mealy really liked him, and she especially liked the queue of people trying to buy from him. In the end she took me to a little kiosk near the beach. I was bored – you could eat any ice lollies that were broken, so I ate quite a lot. There were a lot broken. I didn't get many customers.

Then Mealy taught me how to make candy floss. It was pink and came from pink sugar.

"You pour the sugar in here, look," and she demonstrated with a little jug.

"Now you switch on like this and wait." I watched as it all turned, and strands of spinning sugar threads came out and collected on the side.

"Now use the stick."

I had to use a stick and catch the threads as they spun, to make a big lump of froth on a stick. The kids loved it and sales picked up. But it was all so boring.

Then a fair came and there were rides on the car park right next to me, and the lad in charge of the dodgem cars winked at me and the music blared. I don't really like men winking at me after that Ricky and his antics. But maybe this was different.

"Are you Cathy?" that was the dodgem car lad – he had jumped off the platform and come to see me. He looked a bit greasy close up, with an Elvis quiff. He winked again.

"No, Cathy's dead," I answered, and he looked muddled.

"It's really hot work on the dodgems," he grinned.

I gave him a lolly, which he grabbed and ran off back to his screaming customers. He hung on to the pole of a car and swung one leg out. The top of the pole sparkled as it went round. Sparks were flying everywhere as the cars crashed. The dodgem lad leant over and steered the wheel, the young girl driver gave a loud excited cry as they bumped, and he wound the wheel so fast they went full circle and bumped again.

I felt the thrill and when he looked at me and winked again this time it was different. It was as if the electricity pole was sparking inside me. I couldn't keep my eyes off him now. The music blared and the sun beat down. I was dizzy with excitement and needed another ice lolly to cool off. It was such a nice feeling.

A little kid came to buy a candy floss – I was good at doing it now and got a stick. I switched on and the sugar pink thread spun round the side. I made a lovely pink cloud all stuck together on the stick. I handed it over and the girl handed me a two-shilling piece. I gave her three sixpences and three pennies as change. The little girl went off and I saw her at the shove penny machine and then at the waltzers, then I lost sight of her – until she came back with her mother. The mother was shouting at me.

"You cheating hound, you didn't give Lizzy her change."

"I did I gave her..."

"Where is it then? Cheating a little girl like that, you ought to be sacked..."

"But I gave..."

"Where is it then? You gave nothing, you liar."

I stood there I didn't know what to do. I couldn't just hand her one and nine. It was too much. Then all of a sudden, there stood the dodgem car lad.

"Is everything alright?"

"No, she is a cheat. She has done our Lizzy out of her change."

"I saw her hand it over. I was here. Right here, I saw." He was telling a lie to help me.

The woman sniffed and grabbed Lizzy.

"You've just gone and spent the change, haven't you? You little beggar, wait till I get you home."

She cuffed liar Lizzy over the head and then they were gone. The dodgem lad winked.

"See you tonight. Favour for favour, eh?"

Then he jumped the fence to the bumpers and grabbed the pole that crackled and spat.

My nice feeling had gone. I was worried. Luckily for me, though, Mealy closed my kiosk early and I put the shutters up and caught a bus home. I remembered what Betty had said, "Be careful."

On the bus now, I knew for certain that I wanted to go back to the safety of our old farm and the old bedroom I shared with my sisters. But I had to stay on the bus and go past our lane end and move forward to Sunkstead and my new life.

To cheer myself up I put a down payment on a Dansette record player, from our Katy's catalogue. You got it straight away, which I was pleased about, but I had to pay in instalments every week. Dad thought this was bad, but Mam was pleased because I was supporting our Katy, as she got commission.

My Dansette was deep blue and I just loved it. I only had one record – Gwendy's boyfriend gave it to me. It was a Buddy Holly LP. I played it over and over again, and louder and louder, until I shut out everything and all the world except myself. Nobody and nothing mattered. I shut out Murielle and French lessons, I shut out Lizzie and her cheating and I shut out the dodgem lad. I didn't care any more, I wasn't going backwards or forwards now, I was just there, with the music in my head.

Mam

I liked living at Sunkstead, we had our own television, at last. Sid and Herb had agreed to share the television at Gum, we had it one month, and they had it next month. Sid or Herb carried the great heavy lump from one house to the next, on the first of every month. It must have been heavy because you could see Sid's knees buckle as he rushed in with it.

The kids watched children's hour, whichever house it was in. Now our own telly was in our best room and we could watch what we wanted. It was a bigger screen as well. Our last one was twelve inches and hard to see. Not that any of us had much time to watch it very much, but at least we didn't have to share.

Village Farm house was perfect with its modern kitchen and two downstairs rooms. It was 'olde worlde' and there were wooden beams on the ceilings and little windows which looked so cosy with the curtains and pelmets which I had made.

The only thing was, I needed bedroom furniture. I had brought our beds, but I had left the big old wardrobes behind me at Gum. I needed small bedside cabinets and chairs. I didn't think it worth trying for a lot more money from Herb, so I decided to go to the saleroom again, in Hull, to see what I could get there. I had bought my kitchen cabinet there and I was pleased with that, I could be lucky again.

It was very exciting, just like a competition that I liked so much. Could I do better than the last person who bid? I went every week – I could hardly keep away. I went on the bus to Hull

– the bus stop was only up the road and it was footpaths all the way, so there was no worry about getting my shoes dirty like they did up our lane at Gum. I got off the bus at George Street, and for some reason, I started to think again, about all those years ago when I did embroidery at Madame Clapham's. In those days, I had to turn off to Kingston Square, but there was no need now. The saleroom was just there near the bus stop.

I got an entrance ticket and went in. I always went early, so I could have a good look round. There was a bedside cabinet that would just fit in next to Vi's bed. It's a bit scratched and wood-wormed but I could easily treat it and sand it and varnish it.

I was going to have this whatever happened. The room was packed but nobody much seemed to be bidding.

"Who will give me five pounds?"

Nobody answered. I held my breath. You have to wait and don't seem too eager in this game.

"Who will give me two pounds?"

Nobody.

"Who will give me one pound?"

Nobody.

"Ten shillings then. Surely?"

"Two shillings," I shouted. I did not know where that voice came from, my heart was beating fast.

"Any advance on two shillings. Surely?"

No more bids.

Bang, the gavel went down, and it was mine.

Then I eyed a little dresser in the corner. It would look really good in our room with beams – really cottagey.

I stood there all afternoon – this one was one of the last sales, but I got it. There was somebody bidding behind me, but I kept my hand up showing my ticket. A bit more than I wanted to pay, but I was pleased at the win. It would look lovely when I had finished with it and it would be so good at Village Farm.

Herb went the next day to Hull in our van to collect my trophies. I set to work to get the old varnish off and reveal the wood grain. The little bedside table was a bit disappointing because the top was a veneer and it was not in very good condition.

Vi didn't like it.

"Why are you buying junk for my bedroom?" she shouted, slamming the door as she went upstairs. I can make it look good I know I can, maybe with a lick of paint to match the lilac she had chosen for the walls.

She sounded cross but no more was said. She goes off to work at Cathy's Candy at Ripsea as often as she can. I am pleased she is doing that to earn her pocket money. Herb and I think she should pay a bit towards her keep but I don't like to ask her in case she flies off the handle again. She does that quite a lot these days when I confront her. I hope it's just because she is growing up.

When we had settled in, I decided it was time to have my teeth out. It was free on the National Health now. Herb had already had his out. He had strong teeth really, but he didn't want them to go bad one at a time. Getting false teeth was the new way forwards.

"Better get the job done all at once," he said, "and that will be the end of that." He wanted rid of them before they became big trouble. The worst thing for him was that the dentist had a hard time pulling them out. They were so firmly stuck in, and Herb had to go back a few times until it was all over. Then he could have false teeth.

Everybody I knew had got false teeth except Sid, he decided to pay to get some of his teeth repaired and keep the roots of his old teeth, with false caps stuck in on top. It cost him a fortune. These were not on the National Health. Herb didn't think it was worth it, when you could get false teeth for free.

"He's got a million pounds in his mouth," said Herb jokily, but I have to say Sid's teeth looked good when he smiled. I could not have what he had though, even if Herb agreed to pay, because my gums were bleeding and getting diseased. So, I went to the dentist in Ripsea to have them all out in one go. I had gas, which didn't agree with me, and I went home, in our van with Herb, feeling poorly.

The bleeding wouldn't stop. I held a hanky to my mouth, but soon had to use rags, as the hanky got soaked. I sat up all night hardly daring to move. There was blood everywhere and, next day, Herb took me back to the dentist. There was not much he could do, except tell me to rinse my mouth out with salt and water and take painkillers and go to bed. So, Herb took me back home and I sat and waited. Herb took me back to the dentist the next day.

"I've always had thin blood," I told the dentist and he packed my mouth with cotton wool.

I felt so faint, but that was natural I suppose with losing so much blood. I got the shakes in the end and my whole body was trembling and my little finger was tick, tick ticking, fifteen to the dozen.

'When I have my false teeth in, I'll go to the doctor about my little finger,' I promised myself. Though I know he will just say it is old age. What else can you expect when you're my age?

"You have to just get on with it," he will say. As you get older things start to go wrong and time moves on. You can't go back like that poor woman on the opposite side of the road. Even she knows that and goes forward in the end.

Chapter 15

Interesting times

Me

I don't know why Mam wanted all her teeth out. I remember that she always had a little nick in her front tooth. I liked it being there, somehow, and I asked her about it.

"Why did you have that little groove in your front tooth?" It was like a little tunnel going into her mouth. All the other teeth used to have a smooth line at the bottom edge, but not this one.

"It's because I bite the cotton thread when I am sewing, and it wore away my tooth." Why didn't she use scissors? I thought impatiently but I didn't say anything, I had lost interest.

I was losing interest in a lot of things including going to chapel. Everything was getting boring at home, as well. I used to want everything to stay the same, but now I found it all so boring.

Here at Sunkstead, I had to be a Sunday school teacher. I had always gone to Ringam chapel Sunday school and then at night I went with Mam and Dad to an evening service. I was fed up with Sunday. At night the parson used to give a sermon for about half an hour, and we prayed and sang hymns for the other half hour. All the women wore their best coats and hats and the men wore suits. It was very serious, but I couldn't wait for it to be over.

Now suddenly, I was a Sunday school teacher. The preacher still controlled things and he took one class and I took another. I really liked it at first and tried to make it interesting – I took pictures in and worked on things for the kids to do. But I kept thinking of the dodgem's lad and the excitement and fear. I was bored with chapel and Sunday school I wanted to get away.

And then I did get away for a week. When you were old enough you could go on a holiday, organised by our chapel, to Scarborough, and I couldn't wait.

First of all, though, Brenda came to our house on Friday night to get my hair ready. My old style was no good now – flat to my head was not in fashion these days and not at all with it, but I could still have my kiss curls.

Brenda's hair was fantastic – she had a huge beehive made from expert backcombing. You had to have a special comb, and Brenda had one. Brenda worked all over my head, first taking a long strand and backcombing it into a tangle under the front strands. Then she combed the top lightly to give a smooth blob. It made my hair look high and round. Then Brenda used some hairspray – it was even stronger than the lacquer Shirley used. I started to cough, and my eyes tingled.

The result was good, though not quite as good as Brenda's own. I was very pleased and hoped that it would all stay in place for a day or two. I would buy myself a better comb and spray as soon as I could, at Scarborough.

There was a whole gang of us who were fifteen years old that year from our area. Mam lent me her embroidery case. She had to take her embroidery out and pack it in a drawer. It was only small, but it didn't matter because I hadn't got many clothes to take. I had my new vanity case to hold all my make-up and that was the important thing. I was soon packed and ready for my holiday.

We seemed to be on the bus for ages, picking up other people from our villages. We had three vicars, but not ours from Ringam, and they all stood up when we got to Green Gates Hotel. Three white haired men in suits organised us like an army. First one got up and went to the hotel door and the second one stood at the bottom of the bus steps, to help us all off and make sure we didn't fall. I thought that they were so old, they were more likely to fall than me. The last one signalled which group had to stand next and make their way (carefully) to the hotel.

I had never seen anything like it. All those people my age dashing about with suitcases and looking good and looking as if they knew where they are going. I didn't know where I was going, how could I? I had never done this before.

The hotel was past its best with faded cream walls and brown canvas flooring. It was old-fashioned, and our bedroom was the same. There were two ancient ladies sitting on wooden chairs on the landing. They wore hats, not little hats like Mam still made for Grandma. These were big hats – the sort ladies wear when they go out, but these stayed put. They just sat there in brown and grey clothes. Their pleated skirts hung like dead fish, as they stared without speaking.

I went to bed early, in a room I shared with a girl from Hull called Olive. She was quite a lot older than me, but I liked her because she smiled like Amy. We made a lot of noise laughing, so it was ages before I went to sleep – only to be woken at six in the morning as they shook me urgently. They were lads. Lads in my bedroom and I was in my nighty – what were they doing?

"Come on with us, we are going swimming, hurry up." I pulled the Sellotape off my kiss curls, so quickly that my cheeks were stinging. I hoped that my beehive was still in place.

Swimming in the cold Great North Sea at this time in the morning, I had never heard of anything so silly. But what fun. I got up and went with them with my new swimming costume under my dress. I put my high heels on to look good, but it meant that I could hardly keep up with everybody.

We met a whole group on the valley road to the beach, the sun was only just up, and so it was cold, but they all stripped to their swimming cossies and jumped in the waves. I took my dress off and stood on the side, shivering in my unused costume – I couldn't swim, but I think I looked good because a fabulous blonde lad came up to me and asked me if I was going in the water. He ran straight down to the sea, tossed his jumper off, pulled his trousers off, and underneath were his snazzy swimming trunks. I watched his tanned muscular legs.

There was a lot of laughing and splashing before they all got out. Then on the way back, the good-looking blonde lad walked with me – he noticed me! He still had his wet shorts on and his towel round his neck. He put his jumper on me.

"You look cold," he said.

"So do you," I answered and he rubbed his hands on my cheeks, I felt giddy and suddenly hot.

We walked together so closely that our hands clashed together, once by accident, I felt that electricity again, like I felt when I looked at the dodgem car lad. Only this time, it was much better and not frightening. Then all of a sudden, he grabbed my hand and squeezed it. Two of his mates turned up and they started talking about playing billiards. We went through the door and he let go of my hand.

"See ya," he shouted and bounded up to his room on the third floor. I passed the two old ladies sitting on the landing chairs – I wondered if they had been there all night just sitting and watching.

"Be careful," one of them said as I dashed past them. What's she talking about? What does she know about this excitement I have inside my belly?

Olive was just getting up.

"I've met the most gorgeous lad," I shrieked as I faced her, with my back pushing the door closed.

"I saw you coming in with him when I looked through the window." Our room had a huge bay window facing the main drive. It was old and the paint was peeling and there was a cold draught coming in at the sides.

"He comes to our chapel in Hull. He used to teach at our Sunday school, but he has left now he's going to college to teach."

Oh, wow, I just couldn't get enough. I wanted to hear more and more about him. It was all so exciting.

"What is he called?"

"He calls himself Hank."

"Is that his real name?"

"No, he's really called Howard, but for some reason he suddenly said that he wanted to be called Hank a few weeks ago."

Hank, Hank, Hank. Oh, I will call him Hank. I really like that name. I hugged it to myself.

The next day I went for breakfast and Hank came and sat next to me. He was in white shorts and jumper and had white sandshoes on. He put his tennis racquet at the side of his chair. He talked all the time to his mate Ray. Olive was next to me.

"Hey, look at this," said Hank, and he turned the drinking glass upside down to show us all. I looked, and embossed underneath was the word 'Durapex'. It was the name of the firm that made the glasses. I knew that.

"What does that remind you of?" He was grinning.

"Just take two letters out," said Ray and he laughed out so loud he started to choke and had to have a drink of water. Olive raised her eyes to heaven and smiled. I didn't know what they were talking about. I didn't see what was funny. Which two letters?

"We're off for tennis." Hank got up and handed me his tennis racquet. I stood there with it, watching him in his tennis outfit and white short shorts. He combed his blonde hair in a quiff, put his comb back in his pocket and then took his racquet off me. He took my hand and we trotted off with his tennis partner friend, Ray.

"Wish I'd brought my car," he shrugged, "it would be much easier."

Have you got your own car then?"

"Yes, it's a red Morris Mini Minor."

It was a long walk and a bus ride, but I was happy enough just holding his hand and then sitting patiently on the side of the tennis court when he played. He won. After tennis his hand was hot and sweaty as we made our way back to the hotel.

"See ya," he shouted as he bounded the stairs. It was like that for the next few days. I did what he said, and he talked about himself, and every night at the stone bridge he bent and kissed me. It was our place between streetlights.

This wasn't like that Ricky at the cricket ground in Ringam, for a start I liked what Hank was doing this time and he didn't push at me, he was gentle. I felt so safe and excited at the same time. I loved his caring face and his blonde lock of hair falling over his eyes. I snuggled towards him. He held me to him.

Hank. It was all so different and so exciting. The world looked full of colour and I felt that I was floating about with my feet hardly touching the ground. All the houses and trees seemed unreal and bright. They weren't the same old colours that I had seen before.

At night, we all got together in the common room and talked about 'life'. I had never thought about 'life', I just lived it. But these lot here talked about it. What to do about it, how to get on and impress. I was impressed with them all.

They had told their parents what they were going to do in life and what they wanted. They all said that their parents were no good and didn't understand. Well I didn't understand. So, I said nothing to these amazing people.

Then one night, Hank had a good idea. He said, "Follow me," and I did as I always did, I trooped after him. His mate, Ray, came with him and we ran down the dark corridor which led to the bedrooms. We went in one of them and saw where the white-haired men slept.

This was exciting beyond belief. Here were underpants, false teeth containers and medical creams for strange 'down below' conditions. We laughed so much my sides ached. Then Hank got a water jug from the bedside and tipped it on the bedding. We shrieked with laughter and he went round all the beds wetting them as if the grey haired men hadn't been able to get to the toilet. It was so funny. We ran off breathlessly and went to our own rooms. Even when I was curled up in my own bed I couldn't stop laughing.

In the morning I was called to the office. Hank had apparently confessed and told them that I was doing it too. The men were very angry.

"You are spoiling your chances in life," said one, "we are debating whether to tell your parents."

They said it was very serious. I couldn't see what was so serious, it was only fun. These were such old-fashioned men. I could not see what all the fuss was about. I just shrugged and came out to find Hank and his gang. But I couldn't find him. Hank never seemed to be around now.

But I was sure that he really loved me. Of course, it was the trouble we were in that kept us apart. Strange though, it was only me that had to be called back to the interview room with the boring old men, again and again.

"You must face up to what you have done, young lady," said one of the men sitting behind a desk. "As you sow so shall ye reap. We are still debating whether to contact your parents."

What were they talking about? I couldn't think why they were making all this fuss. I was in love and I bet they were jealous.

"See ya," shouted Hank as I got on our bus home. I recognised his voice and turned to see him combing the quiff in his hair and smiling.

When I got home, nobody was very bothered about me. Mam was worried about something and they were all thinking about her and not me. She went around with a frown on her face. But I didn't think about that because I was thinking about Hank.

I was full of excitement when I got up that morning. Will Hank be there at our door? Will he have come in his little red car to see me? When I pull the curtains back, will I see him looking up at my window? He wasn't there. But he could come at any time. He has his own car, hasn't he?

I waited for Hank every day. Some days I went to Ringam to see Suzy and I told her all about Hank.

"He has blonde hair and he is thin and tall and so-o gorgeous; I will bring him to see you when he comes." She said she couldn't wait.

My heart ached for Hank and I have been waiting up at night curled on our new couch. Well I say 'new', but it is an old one from a saleroom in Hull. Mam likes going there. She goes every week and brings back junk which she 'does up'. Our house smells of turps and cleaning stuff if she has bought furniture like tables. If she has bought furniture like armchairs and couches there is material all over for a few days, while she fits a new cover.

Well, I go on our couch, which is in the corner, and above on a shelf is our wireless. It isn't 'wireless' because there are wires all over and there is a wonky aerial, which you have to move about to get reception. Then you move a big dial to get weird sounds and crackling and then Radio Luxemburg comes through. I love Luxy and I listen, imagining that Hank is listening, wherever he is. We were sending each other messages of love. I think of my own heartbeat when my favourite song comes on, and I think about it missing a beat when he kisses me.

I didn't want to tell Mam about my holiday – she wouldn't understand about being in love. She is too old.

Anyway, thank goodness, she has a little baby boy grandson to think about now. I saw her face light up when our Katy brought him home. Katy had to move from their flat, the owner had said 'no children allowed' there. They got a mortgage on a lovely little house in a village near Hull. I think the person renting was taken by surprise, our Katy was a good payer and now she had moved. It wouldn't be easy to replace two good and reliable lodgers.

"As you sow so shall you reap," said Dad and I didn't know what that had to do with anything, except that I had heard it from that vicar, when I was on holiday.

I don't care anyway; I am so in love with Hank. Surely, he will come and see me soon in his little red car? He will take me away from all this.

I heard Mam and Uncle Sid whispering again that afternoon. When Hank takes me away, I won't even care about what they are saying.

Mam

When our Vi came back from her holiday in Scarborough she seemed to be in such a bad mood. It has not done her much good going away, she still looks so sulky.

"Did you have a good time?" I asked, but she didn't answer and just took my grey case upstairs and slammed her bedroom door. Whatever could be wrong? I was angry and thought of going upstairs and having it out with her and make her face up to her bad manners. I never treated my dear mother like that, at least I don't think I did.

But I had not got the energy to face Vi, somehow, I would have done at one time and spoken to her in no uncertain terms. I used to have so much energy, I would go out to do the milking with Herb and then make breakfast for us all. I would sew and knit for the girls and after cleaning the house I would be out again doing the evening milking. I just can't do that now. I've stopped evening milking and Terry comes to milk the cows with Herb and often Stewy comes after school. I am not myself. I think I will go to Doctor Newby and see if he can give me a tonic. I will tell him about my little finger as well.

I sat for ages in that little waiting room with Mrs Newby sitting bolt upright at her desk. The phone rang and she had to dash outside and back into her own house. They really did need a door putting in so that she could just walk through from this little room and straight into her own house.

I waited an hour or so until it was my turn. I sat there in my best suit and head-scarf and when I finally saw the doctor, I started to cry. He looked shocked and I must say, I was surprised at my own behaviour, as well.

"I only need a tonic, Doctor Newby. I am just feeling a bit run-down. My time of life you know, I should think."

He looked at me and held my hands. He looked at me again.

"When did this start?"

"What?"

"This trembling, in your left finger."

"Oh, I can't really remember. It's been like it for quite a while now. I expect it is just old age. Nothing that a tonic can't cure."

"A tonic won't cure this. Have you lost your sense of smell by any chance?"

"Oh yes, years ago we all think it's funny..." I stopped because he wasn't smiling.

"I can't be sure of course, but I think that you have got Parkinson's disease."

"What's that? What's going to happen?"

"Well let's not get ahead of ourselves." He smiled and started writing a letter. He stood up.

"Give this to Mrs Newby when you go out and we will see what the specialist thinks." That serious non-smile look, again.

"Goodbye."

I went home on the bus, hardly able to take in what he had said. Had I got the dropsy? Or Saint Vitas dance? What was it I had got? What if I ended up like that woman who takes two steps forwards and one step backwards? I wish Doctor Newby had given me a tonic, though. Maybe the chemist at Ringam could help.

Just as I got off the bus Sid arrived all dressed up ready to go to a Councillors meeting in Hull. I went with him into our kitchen.

"How's tricks?"

"Not too good. The doctor thinks I have Parkinson's disease," I whispered.

"I don't know anything about it. Have you talked to Herb?"

"I haven't had time yet, I will, after milking, but I don't want the girls to know anything just yet."

I did talk to Herb, but he didn't know anything either.

"Mebbie he is wrong. You could just be run-down. Let's wait for the specialist."

"What about going private?"

"Yes, we can but let's wait and see, shall we?"

I did not have to wait long; an appointment came that week.

But before we went to the hospital appointment, our vicar phoned for an appointment of a different kind. He wanted to see Herb and me and could he come on Sunday when Vi was teaching at Sunday school? She could teach both classes. She was quite capable.

He came that Sunday afternoon. Herb and I sat there in our clean clothes. What could he want?

"This is a delicate matter," he cleared his throat. "It seems that all was not well on the holiday at Scarborough. Has your daughter talked to you about it?"

What on earth was the matter? What could she have done? I bet it was a lad, that's it – that's what all the silent treatment has been about in the last few days. That is why she has been stuck in her bedroom playing that record player at full volume. She thinks that she is in love. Somebody she met on holiday is hardly the basis for love though, is it? I hope she hasn't done anything silly.

"Is it about her getting a boyfriend?" I asked.

"Ah, well it is something to do with a boy." He shifted uneasily and pulled at his dog collar. He looked out of the window. I hope he noticed my pretty curtains.

"They got into a compromising position, so to speak."

"Surely not, she knows what's what our Vi, doesn't she, Herb?"

Herb nodded and said "Aye."

"There must be some mistake," I said.

"That's what I thought, but I have it on good authority that your daughter was involved in an unsavoury business."

"What sort of business?" We were all feeling uncomfortable.

"She went in the staff bedrooms with some boys..."

"Oh no."

"And messed up their rooms."

I could see Herb relax.

"I have been given the task of letting you know. I am sure one of the lads was the ringleader. We will say no more. Least said soonest mended."

He gave a sigh.

"Can we pay for any damage?" I asked, though I knew it would have to be from Herb's money and I had not asked him yet.

"No, no – no permanent damage, thank you."

"Pretty curtains," he said as he got up to leave.

We decided not to say anything to Vi – maybe it was just high jinks. In any case, I had not got the energy at the moment and we had enough to think about.

Chapter 16

Results

Me

After I got back from Scarborough my O level results came. I was in bed when I heard the postman – he pushed the mail through our letter box. I heard it creak, then snap; I bet he had to be careful with his fingers. It's time somebody put some oil on it.

"Letter for you," Mam shouted up the stairs. I turned over and went back to sleep.

Mam brought the letter to me with my mug of tea. It was ten o'clock in the morning, I heard the church clock strike, but I still needed some more rest. I wish she would stop bothering me.

"This came for you. It looks like your results."

"Just leave it on the side. On that awful bedside cabinet." I turned away without opening my eyes I needed to get some more sleep.

"Aren't you going to read it?"

"Not now."

But as soon as she had gone, I sat up in bed and ripped open the envelope. The subjects were all listed, in typing, on the left and the percentages had been written in with a fountain pen on the dotted line. Probably Mr Sparrow had done that for everybody who had taken exams. I expect he didn't have anything better to do in his holidays. He was probably still sitting in that great big office of his.

I had passed them all with quite good marks. I had even passed French and had eighty-five per cent in maths. Well, so what? What's the point if I don't have Hank? I let the letter fall onto the floor. Hank hadn't been to see me, was there still time? The summer holiday wasn't over yet, was it?

Then I heard the downstairs door open and the whispering start again. Uncle Sid must have come.

"Wsss, wsss, wsss,"

I jumped out of bed and put my ear to the wooden floor, at the side of the carpet. But nothing was clear except a hissing. I expect they were talking about how awful I was and how I wouldn't open my letter. Anyway, they don't know how good my results are. I gulped my tea, it was cold, yuk. Then I went to our bathroom and stayed there, plucking my eyebrows using Mam's tweezers. I can't imagine she ever used tweezers, her eyebrows were so wild and woolly. I heard a car door slam and I knew that Uncle Sid had gone. I went downstairs and there was Mam wanting to know my results, well, she could read them from Mr Sparrow's stupid letter, couldn't she? She rushed upstairs to get the bit of paper, then she was on the phone to Mrs White.

It was Veronica's mam who wanted her daughter to go to Oxford.

"No messing about after A levels, it is straight to Oxford for Veronica," she said, in her plummy voice. Mam knew her from Ringam WI, where Mrs White was president – trust her to have the top job.

Anyway, I couldn't be bothered with all that. I wasn't bothered about Veronica. I was only bothered about Hank.

I did some more work at Cathy's Candy for the last few weeks of the holiday. I was in a kiosk near the waltzers this time. Thank goodness I didn't have to watch that stupid lad on the dodgems, he really fancied himself and Hank was a million times more good-looking than him.

Roy Orbison sang about being lonely and I cried buckets because only I knew what he meant. I longed for Hank and I felt so alone – just like in the song. Hank still hadn't come in his little red car. Maybe he wasn't going to come, I couldn't bear it.

"Hey penny for them, love? Candy floss when you're ready."

"Oh sorry," I talked through my tears, as I started up the machine. Round and round went my stick and my tears hit the metal bowl on the side and went bright pink.

"Cheer up, love, it might never happen – unless it already has. Ha, ha."

"It has."

The candy floss got bigger and bigger as my stick whirred round.

"Ah, boyfriend trouble is it? You'll soon find somebody else. Don't worry, love."

A dagger went through my heart – no, never anybody else – I said to myself as Roy Orbison sang about a new romance. I would never take that chance.

"Hey! I think that's big enough. Stop that thing, love."

I looked down and the glob of pink sugar strands was bigger than her head. I shrugged and handed it over. It was only when she had gone off with her trophy that I realised she hadn't paid.

Mrs Mealy seemed to come from nowhere. Suddenly, she was there, trust her to come when I had forgotten to charge that woman. I opened the till and jigged about with the money, pretending that I had coins in my hand. I wasn't sure she was fooled, and I blushed bright red. To tell the truth, I hadn't sold much all morning – maybe I hadn't noticed the customers.

'Please don't send me home,' I pleaded inside my head.

I need to earn money to buy that short skirt from our fabulous new C&A clothes shop in Hull. I earned one shilling an hour but, even though it wasn't hard, it was boring. I badly needed the money. I badly needed a new skirt – a shop bought one – not one that Mam made. I needed to be in fashion in case Hank came.

Mealy fished in the till, clattering the coins, and took all the money out and stuffed it into a leather pouch round her neck.

"Break at twelve," she said on her way to her next kiosk near the dodgems. I could see the back of her greasy hair hanging down her shoulders. 'I'm never going to be like that – she doesn't care about how she looks – it's all about money with her.'

Brian turned up at twelve to give me half-an-hour break. There was hardly time to go to 'spend a penny' then eat my sandwich. But I did manage to have a quick walk on the sands, I loved searching the tide line. I was lucky, this time, because in the bits of seaweed I found a lovely shell. It was a bi-valve and wasn't damaged at all. It had little ridges all the way down, and towards the pointed end it was pink. I ran my thumbs over it and marvelled at its structure. There were rays coming from the pointed end and going to the rim. It looked just like the sun rising on a new day. That had to be a good sign. I would keep it as a good luck treasure for ever.

"D'you fancy a go on the waltzers at five?" asked Brian, when I got back. I was a few minutes late – well ten minutes late to tell the truth. I did it on purpose, thinking that it would make the first hour of the afternoon go quicker. Brian had quite a posh voice, but he tried to sound casual and with it.

"Ye, OK," I said, not looking at him. I shrugged to show that I didn't mind one way or the other.

All afternoon I dreaded going on the waltzers, I knew that I would feel dizzy and would feel so daft if I was sick. I'm no good on that sort of thing. I have always hated roundabouts. And I am still waiting for Hank.

Mam

Herb came with me for the appointment at the hospital. We went in our big new Zephyr car. I wore my navy suit and Herb wore his best suit – the one he had bought for Katy's wedding and the one he would be wearing for Gwendy's wedding. I tried not to think about that just yet, but I was so looking forward to it. Gwendy will make a lovely bride.

I had some tests first, about whether I could feel things when they were pressed on my skin. I could. I had to walk in a straight line, and balance on one leg then the other. I had my reflexes tested – every time I had a test the specialist said "Good," and "Well done". I had to hold his hand and grip it tight, first with my left hand then my right hand. I was very strong with all the farm work I had done, and I think he was impressed because he nodded and smiled at me. He had a lovely smile and he was so smart in his grey suit. I could tell it was hand-finished.

I had a blood test – well my blood was always good even though I had lost a lot when I had my teeth out. I am sure nothing would show up there except that it was thin.

I was going to be alright. I was going to be lucky.

The specialist sat back in his chair, he was only young not much older than Katy. He leant forward and smiled his lovely smile.

I was going to be alright.

"I think that it is fairly clear to me that you have got Parkinson's disease."

"What?" I didn't really take in what he was saying. He could not know for sure, could he?

"What about the blood test?"

"We are ruling out anything else, with the blood test, but I don't expect that we will find anything. There isn't a definitive test for Parkinson's disease – as I say we rule everything else out."

"Are you sure?"

"Yes. In my experience, I can say, yes."

What experience has he got? He could be wrong. But in the bottom pit of my stomach I knew he was right.

"What happens now?" I was suddenly in a foreign land and I had no idea what to do.

"I can give you some relaxants and iron, as you are probably anaemic. The blood test will show that. But, at this moment in time, there is nothing more I can do for you."

"Is that it?" I blurted, forgetting my manners in my desperation. My head-scarf fell to the floor.

"Yes, for now. But don't be too glum, it is surprising what research is being done and you never know when there will be a breakthrough. A cure could be just on the horizon. I will see you again in six months, take this card to the receptionist. She will also give you a carbon copy of my information sheet about the disease."

I forgot to ask for the sheet.

I wasn't the same person that went into the hospital. I was a Parkinson's disease patient. I could not be like other people ever again, it was like walking around with a big black cloud over my head. I walked slowly while everybody else seemed to be skipping along.

Could everybody tell I was poorly? Everyone was carrying on as normal, how could they when I had just been told I had a disease? The world would never be normal for me again. Thoughts fell in and out of my scrambled brain.

"Mebbie he's wrong," said Herb, holding my elbow and steering me to our car. I know he was trying to comfort me and make the best of things, but they can't all be wrong. I did not answer but pulled away from him. I didn't need holding up, I was quite capable of walking.

I sat in our car and looked out of the window, Herb drove us home in silence. My left finger started to tick. I held it with my right hand to steady it, but I could still feel that ticking time bomb tick, tick-ticking and there was nothing I could do about it.

I won't tell the girls about the result of my visit, just yet, in any case there could be nothing to tell. Things could just get better. You hear about it don't you? Suddenly people getting up and walking... if you have faith. I have faith and I pray to God that I will have a miracle cure. If I do get better, I will try harder not to nag Herb again. I will try harder to understand Vi, and I will visit Grandma more often. God, please help me.

Vi had such good results for her O levels, I am so pleased. Mrs White, Veronica's mother, was quite taken aback when she heard. Veronica had not done so well, and she was expected to get ninety-five per cent for the lot, if her mother is to be believed. I must say, I did show off a bit you can't blame me, can you? A daughter of ours going into the sixth form. I have two things now, to take my mind off my illness, which might get better anyway.

Mind you, I worry about Vi's health. She needs to settle down and take things easy, I think. Not strain herself, and take care of herself but she won't listen to me, so what can I do?

Then it was Gwendy's wedding. I bought her dress, and she looked so beautiful with her hair bouffant and little curls framing her face. She married in Beverley, where all her friends were now, and at the reception hotel you could see the magnificent Minster through the window.

I bought my own outfit as well; it was a dusky pink fitted suit. I felt good. Two daughters married and one grandson.

Our Vi refused a new outfit, she said that she was too busy. But she wore a dress I had made her last year and joined in with all the celebrations. I was so thrilled – some of my sisters and brothers came, and it was so nice to be together.

Then it was back down to earth at Village Farm. We had, of course, come home in time for evening milking, but I was happy. I almost forgot about the hospital.

The next night it was our WI meeting in the village hall opposite. It was easy because all I had to do was get changed, and then wait for the hall to be unlocked by Doris, and then wait for the first people to arrive. I could sit down and watch at home, and just by looking through the window, I knew when to get up and go.

Sid turned up unannounced as usual all dressed up – going to a Council meeting. He asked, "How's tricks?" I whispered what had happened at my hospital appointment, but I tried to brush it off, as if it didn't matter too much.

I told him about the WI competition. We always had a competition and this time it was 'a flower from your garden'. I had a lot to choose from now Herb had made a beautiful flower garden where there used to be a piggery. There were hollyhocks taller than me and marigolds as big as tea plates. He had planted bright red roses and they were climbing the brick wall and heading over the top.

But I chose dandelions, as bright as the sun on a summer's day.

"Why choose that when you have so much more?" asked Sid.

I didn't truthfully know but I said, "They're so bright and have survived all that weeding and even though they are not really wanted, they are still pushing through."

"Hmm," said Sid. "It's surprising what they can do these days, you know. There is research going on all the time. You never know when there could be a breakthrough."

I put the dandelions crowded together in a dark blue jug. It really did look like the sun shining in a blue sky. The speaker had to judge, she had been talking about keeping bees and she explained how healthy honey is. I bought a pot there and then.

The idea suddenly came to me, I don't know why I had not thought of it before. I must keep heathy in every way that I can. I must eat healthy, natural food.

I knew that I had been putting weight on recently. I think it was the worry – and the fact that I had not been doing as much physical work as I used to. I will lose some weight. I will help myself and, God willing, I will manage. I felt so positive, now I knew what I had to do.

Then, when I went to collect my jug at the end of our meeting – there was a First Prize notice next to my dandelion arrangement. I could hardly believe it. The speaker had written 'Nature is wonderful' on my card. I was on cloud nine when I crossed the road and went through our front door.

Chapter 17

Settling down

Me

I'm going out with Bri now, (I call him Bri because it sounds more with it than 'Brian') he is a very kind person. It just sort-of happened after the ride on the waltzers with him. We got in this great big round 'cup thing' with a seat. The seat was quite small, so we had to sit close together. The big cup went round, then it started spinning as well. I was very dizzy, I had thought I would be, but Bri put his arm round me and so I didn't say anything.

"Shall we go again?" he asked. I still didn't say anything. The machine finally stopped spinning, but my head did not stop. I felt so poorly, I couldn't answer so he paid, and we went round again. I just closed my eyes and kept very still, waiting for it all to end. I staggered off when it finally stopped and tried to take deep breaths, without Bri noticing. We walked to the bus stop together and I linked arms with him so that I could keep upright. 'Deep breaths, deep breaths,' I told myself and it seemed to work. On the bus home I slumped sideways onto the window in a hot sweat. And it wasn't until I got off at my stop that I felt something like normal and my legs started to go from jelly to solid. I looked for Hank's little red car outside our house, but it wasn't there.

Bri lived in Ripsea now, so he only had a short walk home. He was an only child and lived with his mam (he called her Ma) and his dad (he called him Pa). My mam was pleased because she said his parents worked for the Council – I suppose she thought that was respectable. They had moved to Ripsea so that they could both work at the municipal offices. I got along alright with Bri. He was in the year above me, so I didn't see him much at school, but we started going out and he was my 'steady'.

I thought that Sandra was a steady friend, she was really, but she left school suddenly, even though she had done well with the O levels she had taken. She went to work in a bank in Hull and I had nobody to sit with in registration. Then I heard that Brenda had left school, as well, to work in a shop in Hull and I had nobody to save my seat and sit with on the bus. For all these years, since we were five, Brenda had sat with me going to school and coming home and now, she was gone.

Thank goodness Amy stayed on into the sixth form, we did the A levels together.

A levels were difficult, and I hardly had time to do anything else except study. I must pass these exams, and to do that I had to work. I had thought that after my O levels I would have a good understanding, but it didn't seem as if I had. All this seemed new.

"You have to go into the subject in so much more depth," said my chemistry teacher, "so you really have to start again."

That was a big disappointment. I thought that I would easily understand the subjects, but I didn't. I thought that I had better do something about it. I decided to give up my music lessons straight away, so I had more time to concentrate on my school exams.

"Don't do that," begged Mam. "You are doing well now with your Grade 5 exam." She really wanted me to be good at playing the piano, like she was. She hadn't had the chance to take exams and she saved our family allowance to pay for my lessons. Mam was very good at playing the piano, it seemed to come naturally to her. She could just sit down and play Mozart or Chopin or whoever, without any music. I couldn't do that.

"All my money will be wasted if you give up now," she said. But I was sure that I had tried hard to be like her, and I couldn't be. The fortune teller had not been right, I wasn't like my mam. I needed to get away from here and move on. I was different and if I didn't get on with my exams it would be a disaster for me.

Then, Mam told me that she had a bit of a disaster as well. She said that she had been to the infirmary in Hull for some tests and that she has a disease. But she was still doing morning milking like she always had. She put on her brown milking coat first thing, then she was dashing about cooking my breakfast. One of the lads, Terry or Stewy, came up from Gum to help with evening milking. She was still sewing every day and working on her embroidery and playing the piano. She was cleaning and cooking all our meals, but she only had three to cook for now, so it was all a lot easier. And last night after WI she came back smiling because she had won the flower arrangement competition. I am sure that I would be hopeless at flower arranging. I'm not interested anyway. I am not like her.

I just had to concentrate on my exams. I need to get out of here. I want more experiences, more life and more fun. I want my own money and not always have to ask a man for it. I don't want just the same old things that my mam has settled for.

One good new thing though, was our School and Farm Link Scheme. Uncle Sid had a letter from the Hull Education department asking if we would 'like to participate'.

There was lots of whispering with Uncle Sid and my mam, in the kitchen.

In the end Dad and Uncle Sid decided to volunteer our farms.

"It would be a good idea," said Uncle Sid. "It will make us a modern and forward-thinking farm." Dad didn't answer. He didn't push forwards, he just wanted to get on with looking after his animals.

Strangely though, it ended up with Dad enjoying it all. We were linked up with a secondary school near Hessle Road, in Hull. I thought of Shirley, at the hospital, who was from Hessle Road. I wondered how she was getting on. I wanted her to help me with my hair again. I wanted to learn how to backcomb, even better than I could now. I was sure that she had changed to a bouffant beehive ages ago. I bought some big rollers from

Timothy Whites and Taylors in Hull when I went to my last music lesson. Did Shirley use these modern rollers? I bet she did now.

Poor Miss Brown, my music teacher, didn't know what to say to me. I suppose that last lesson was a cheat really, as I hadn't practised, and she didn't feel it was worth teaching me anything. She sat in silence with her old skirt hanging between her knees. I could see her fat legs and swollen ankles.

I played my pieces, gave her the money, and left. I didn't look back into the room, but I know she was still sitting there on a hard, wooden chair staring at the keys on her grand piano. I went down the dark corridor and into the Hull air. It wasn't fresh air, but it was better than the mouldy moth-air in Miss Brown's house.

I closed the door and stood for a minute. Through the open window I heard her playing slow, beautifully sad notes. I thought of Hank and what might have been. I began to realise that he would never come to see me. I thought of Buddy Holly and how he had died in a plane crash and how he still sang to me from my record player. How could such beautiful people disappear from my life? The pain was strong and sharp in my heart.

Tears came into my eyes and ran down my face, I hoped somebody was watching as I stood there outside Miss Brown's window. I fiddled about in my bag and fished out my mirror. I saw my sad face with real tears running down and I cried some more. Then I set off to catch the trolley bus for the last time. Everybody walked past me, getting on with their lives, but nobody could know my magnificent sadness. It was as if I was standing on a stage acting a part that I didn't know how to play.

'Look at me,' I wanted to shout, 'I have been in love and felt the pain. I have been in a different world, with bright colours and music. I have been where no one has been before and walked on air. I want to go back there again.' But I didn't, I just went home.

I had given up with playing the piano, I couldn't do it any more. But I could do exams and that is what I was going to do. I would get good results and leave home.

And there was something else to think about just now. It was the Farm Link Scheme. You see my dad wanted somebody to go with him to their School Speech Day. One day a letter came through our letter box (it still hadn't been oiled and went with a bang when anything came). It had a postmark saying 'Kingston upon Hull' so it looked posh. It was a card edged with maroon – an invitation for Dad and Mam to be guests of honour at their Speech Day. Nobody wanted to go. Dad never liked that sort of thing and Mam didn't want to go either. I was surprised because she liked dressing up and posh things.

"You should go, Herb," she said. "The farm should be represented – after all you have done for the school."

She also said that I should go with Dad. I was keen. I was used to the pupils and they would know me. You see when they came round the farm in their maroon uniforms and sturdy black shoes (wellies would have been better), it was me who stood with Dad, as he talked about the animals. He gave them wire baskets and they were allowed to gather the eggs. I always collected the eggs every day after school – it was boring to me, but these kids didn't know about hens laying eggs – they just went to Hull shops and got them in boxes. They were excited now.

"Hens lay one egg every day. Sometimes they are double yolked like this." Dad held out a big egg – ridged and long – we weren't allowed to sell these as they didn't fit in the boxes, so we ate them. It was really good if you got one, your breakfast was twice the size. They all stared at what Dad held in his mucky hand.

"I wish I had one of them for breakfast," said one of the lads licking his lips. "But if that egg comes out of its bum, I don't fancy that."

"Bet it hurt," said another, squatting down and pretending to lay an egg.

"Squawk, squawk."

Dad didn't bother with what they were saying. He took them to our cow house and showed the cows being milked. They went to our dairy and saw the milk being sloshed in buckets and then filtered and cooled.

"Our milk is in a bottle on our doorstep," said one of the girls standing back from the action.

"I'm glad I don't have to see this every day. It puts me off."

"Hey, look at that one weeing."

"It might go in the milk."

I watched all this and moved them on when Dad went to the next set of animals. He answered questions that the teacher made them ask.

So, you see, I was a good one to go to their Speech Day. Mam bought me a red sheath dress from our Katy's catalogue, she seemed to have gone off sewing all my clothes, thank goodness. I was pleased to see that the hem was above my knees, but she knows I don't like red. It doesn't suit me.

"It was in the sales section," was all she would say. The good thing was, it fitted me – like a glove and I looked quite good. I put my rollers in my hair the night before and slept in them, even though it felt like a hedgehog was on my head. Dad wore his best suit and Mam bought him a new tie.

We had a good time and we were treated like VIPs. The kids waved to me and giggled. Me and Dad stepped out following the Headmaster, and we sat next to him on the stage. I could see that Dad wasn't comfortable, but I could tell that he felt proud as well. It was as if we were royalty.

Then, it was back to studying. I bet royalty hadn't to do this. I had to go to Hull library to look stuff up because Ripsea library was small and our school library didn't have the detailed science books. Buckingham Palace would have the best research books money could buy. I had to chug to Hull on our cold bus. I slogged on every day and night.

When Bri left school, to take up a job in the office at Cathy's Candy, I hardly noticed. But we saw each other just the same as we always had. I used to go on the bus to Ripsea on Friday and Saturday nights to see him or he came to see me.

Sometimes we stayed in and sometimes we went to the flicks at The Cosy Cinema. On Fridays I caught the bus home at 8pm, I was always tired from studying. On Saturdays I caught the last bus home at 9.30pm. We got into a routine and it suited me well, I was concentrating on something else.

Even looking good started to take a back seat. These exams held the key to my escape. I was going to be important and even famous. I didn't have to be stuck here at Sunkstead all my life – if only I can do these exams.

But I couldn't do exams if I kept on being ill. And I did keep on being ill. I had a cold and a high temperature and couldn't go to school. I can't study if I am poorly. What if I fail these exams?

Mam

Herb was pleased when I got back from our WI and told him that I had won. Vi just went upstairs to her room and put her music on. I wish she would change that record. She plays it over and it's very loud. The ceiling is only wooden, and we can hear everything above.

"Don't get your hopes up too much, love," said Herb when I told him my plan to get healthy.

"But it's a good idea, don't you think?"

"Aye, mebbie."

"Well, it can't do any harm, can it?"

"No, that's true."

I felt a bit down after that, but I was determined to keep to my plan. We always ate healthy meals, as far as I knew. We had our own fresh meat every day, but we have not got our own vegetables any more, and the shop bought ones did not seem very fresh.

"Can I buy vegetables off your hubby?" I asked Doris, when she next came to the village hall. I knew her husband had a big garden on the other side of the village, and his fresh vegetables would be just the thing for me.

"Oh yes, he'll be so pleased that somebody likes what he grows. I get fed up of the mucky stuff he brings into my kitchen. These days I'd rather buy clean ones from March's shop. Let somebody else do all the slog, eh?"

That was that then – the walk down to his garden would help me keep that little bit of extra weight off. And I'd have fresh veg. into the bargain. Then I started drinking the water that I had cooked them in, so that no goodness was lost. I bought Complan from Mrs March. I remember that they used to give it to the soldiers in the war, to help them build up their strength. So, it would be good for me.

"Why don't you try Sanatogen?" asked Mrs March. Did she know I was ill? How could she know? Did I look poorly? Were people looking at my trembling left finger and putting two and two together? I put my left hand in my pocket and bought some Sanatogen. You never know what might help do you? I started to drink it during the day. People say it is good for the brain, so I need that.

And I need to talk to Herb about what is going to happen to Vi.

"What is going to happen to Vi?"

"What do you mean?"

"We need to be thinking about her future."

"What about it?"

"Well what is she going to do?"

"She'll do what she wants – mebbie she'll marry that lad of hers soon."

"I'm not so sure. I think she is after going to university and I don't think that she is strong enough. Maybe we should talk to the Headmaster at parents' evening. Will you come?"

"Aye alright."

He didn't have much to do with the girls' education. I was usually the one who took an interest. But he had signed her school report and now he was saying he would come to the school – so that was a step forward.

Secretly, I hoped that Vi would settle down and marry Brian. He was a steady lad with a steady job and lived locally — she could do worse.

I was pleased with myself about Herb agreeing to come to the school, until I realised that I might have been nagging and I promised God that I would not do that. But sometimes you have to and move things on. I know the best way to get round Herb.

But I had quite a job to persuade Herb and Sid to get involved in the Farm Link Scheme. I whispered to Sid, "Don't you think it would be a good idea, Sid?"

"Yes, it could be, but we are all so busy working on the farm."

"Yes, but your lads are helping now. I know we're flat out, but it's a good thing thinking of town children — we would be doing our bit for society. And I'm sure I could get Herb to talk about the animals and Vi would be good at talking about the science. And she teaches at Sunday school, so she's used to talking to children."

Was I nagging again? I just want what's best for everybody. I've always pushed for that.

Sid and Herb finally agreed that the Farm Link Scheme could go ahead. It seemed to be a great success. I watched the children's eager faces and I felt so proud of the farm then.

When it came to their School Speech Day, I wasn't sure I could go to Hull and walk in the school's hall. I'm not sure that I have the confidence these days. I'll let Vi go.

When I suggested Vi go to Open Day with Herb, he thought it was a good idea. I am a bit hurt that he did not insist that I went.

The Author Studying
By Amy (in the sixth form)

Chapter 18

The plan

Me

When I got better and went back to school everybody, who was anybody, had applied to university or college. I hadn't, and I didn't know how to do it, the deadline was looming. Mam started talking to me about what I was going to do when I left school.

"I really want to go to university." But Mam didn't know if I should. Nobody in our family had done that. Dad was brought into the discussion and then something happened that had never happened before – they both went to our school parents' evening and asked to see Mr Sparrow. I don't know what they said or what he said, but it was decided that I had to go to Teacher Training College.

They probably didn't think I could get good enough grades for university.

I heard Mam whispering to Uncle Sid again. I bet they were talking about how weak and weedy I was.

I had to go with what they said because I had to rely on them for money. Dad's accountant said that I would not get a grant, as Dad and Sid were so 'asset rich', whatever that meant. I never felt rich, I hadn't got assets, unless you counted my Dansette record player. Any money I had, I had earnt myself at Cathy's Candy. Anyway, even though I had to apply to college and not university, I wasn't too worried, I quite fancied teaching. I was quite good at Sunday school and with our Farm Link Scheme.

Amy helped me in the school library. She showed me where the college prospectuses were – in alphabetical order. I got as far as 'B' and plumped for Birmingham because the course was part one-degree level in the sciences. I thought that would be a good start, and so I sent for an application form using Amy's example letter that the class had been given and that I had missed. The application form came by return and I spent a lot of time filling it in, working into the night to do it, as well as my A level work.

The letter, asking me for interview, came quickly. I had to stay overnight. I packed Mam's little grey case with my red sheath dress – I still don't like red, but it shows my figure up well. I grabbed my nighty from my bed and stuffed that in with my toothbrush. I didn't think that I would need make-up.

I went in my school uniform and got on the early bus to Hull. I caught a train from Hull to Manchester where I had to change for Birmingham. I had never been this far on a train before. I had been to Sunkstead from Ripsea on a train once, but that only took twenty minutes, so it didn't really count.

Mam had given me the train fare and £1 extra for emergencies only.

"Don't forget that in a real emergency you can ring us from a phone box," said Mam. "Ask the operator for a reverse charge call. It costs more, so make sure it is a real emergency." I wasn't sure what a real emergency was.

From Victoria station I had to go to Piccadilly station in Manchester. I asked the way from a porter in uniform.

"Go on Corporation Street and then ask again." He pointed the way. Mam said that I could get a taxi if I couldn't walk from one station to the other, but I thought that it would be too much money to spend all in one go. So, I walked and kept asking until I got to Market Street and then after about half an hour, I was at Piccadilly station. I kept asking until I found my train. It was a diesel and swooped me down to Birmingham.

I was so far from home I was completely lost and in a world of strange people rushing about – people that I didn't know, like in Hull, but worse. Funnily enough I didn't feel frightened – I felt as if I was on a big adventure where I made the rules. I smiled at the young girl on the seat opposite in the carriage – she smiled back.

"Hello, I'm Marcia," she said, leaning towards me. She had a very short skirt on – it was shorter than my skirt, even when I rolled the waistband. Her hair was very beehive and she looked top heavy, and really good. She dived into her big crocodile-skin bag and brought out some sandwiches.

"My mam made them – help yourself." They were ham and mustard – I didn't like mustard, but I was starving, so I tucked in anyway.

"Have you got a boyfriend? Mine is so fabulous – Marty. He's older than me and looks like Billy Fury with his blond quiff."

And she started singing, like Billy, with all the body flicks. She held her head down so I could see the top of her beehive and her eyes looked up at me under her fringe. I told her all about Hank.

"Hank!" she shrieked. "What a great name," and we snuggled down together laughing. Why didn't I tell her about Bri?

"I'm going for an interview for the Teacher Training College in Birmingham," I said.

"So am I!"

She was going for the same college as me. How could that happen?

"Is everybody on this train going for interview at our college?" I smiled. "We won't stand a chance." We both shrieked with laughter.

"I don't care if I don't get in," said Marcia. "I might run off with Marty. We are engaged to be married." She showed me a shiny ring on her left hand. It looked like one you could buy in Woolies. She did a quick hand jive.

"I've seen my doctor and I'm going on the contraceptive pill, are you?" Then before I had time to reply, she carried on, "Oh well no, you wouldn't be – you have to be married or engaged and so..." she giggled and snuggled up to me again.

I wonder if Marcia is having sex, she must be so in love with Marty. How exciting.

Everybody was getting married except me.

Marcia fished in her big crocodile-skin bag and brought out a little lilac chiffon scarf and tied it round my neck.

She backcombed my hair and sprayed it.

"That's better, you're not bad looking, you know, when you try." I pulled at the scarf, it made me self-conscious with my white school blouse and blazer, but I got my mirror out of my bucket bag and had a look at my reflection. She was right, it did look good.

We had to get a bus from New Street station, and I was glad Marcia was there because she seemed to know her way around, we were soon signing in at the college Hall of Residence – Marcia wasn't on my floor. I was on my own again.

Next, we all had to do an IQ test in a huge hall and then we could all 'relax', said Matron. I was relaxed anyway and having Marcia with me had made everything more exciting.

"Cook will serve dinner at 7pm."

'That's funny,' I thought, 'we always have our dinner in the middle of the day, at home.'

After dinner, we went to our rooms – I shared with a girl who was wearing a cream suit with a box jacket and had a big case full of things that I hadn't got. She said that her mother had packed her case for her. She had a dressing gown and slippers for a start, and what she called a 'sponge bag'. I had never heard of one, but I saw what was in hers. There were creams and soaps, perfumes and powders and a flannel. We had to go to a room, with a line of sinks, where we all got washed.

Everybody stripped. I stood there in my nighty, staring at their big breasts and their bare bodies. It was like when we showered after hockey at school, except that now we didn't have to wear shower caps and there was no Miss Legg to shout at me and tell me to move.

It took the girls a long time to get ready for bed, they shaved under their arms with little pink razors and washed everywhere – and I mean everywhere. They used special liquid

174

to take make-up off and put night cream on. Then, there was sweet smelling talcum powder flying about, it took my breath away. I only had my toothbrush – I didn't know you had to have a sponge bag and all the other things. I brushed my teeth and then went back to my room and went to bed.

I wore my sheath dress and Marcia's little lilac scarf for my interview – it made me feel modern and think that I didn't care about being interviewed. But I did care, and my voice wobbled when I had to read a passage from a book, in front of three men.

I couldn't believe it when I had read a few lines – it was about a new scheme – The Farm Link Scheme. I knew all about it! They asked me questions about what I had read, and I told them all about my dad and me going to the school Speech Day.

I couldn't stop talking until the man in the middle said, "Thank you that is fine. Now, can you tell us what your father does for a living?"

He must have been asleep, because I had just been telling him about our farm, or maybe he was daft. I thought I'd better answer as if they were all clever and wide awake.

"He is an owner farmer."

"Don't say just farmer or tenant farmer," my mam had said. "Uncle Sid and your dad are owner farmers so make sure you say that." I didn't mention Uncle Sid.

Next, they asked me what I was reading at home – I told them about *The Day of the Triffids*, – I really liked that book, I could hardly put it down until I had read it all.

I was really reading *Trouble with Lichen* now, and it was about women, and choosing between getting married and having babies or having a career. Maybe the contraceptive pill can help us girls, but I thought I had better not say anything about that. I thought of Marcia and I looked at the three old men in front of me, what would she say?

The man on the left stood up and thanked me for coming and I picked up my case and went home – the same way as I came but the other way round. I didn't see Marcia.

I got off the train at Hull and walked to the ticket barrier and handed in my ticket. Then I looked up. Mam, looking anxious clutching her handbag, and Dad, wearing his trilby and with his pipe clenched in his mouth, were waiting there for me.

Mam

I did not like her going on a train on her own. What if she got lost? She has never travelled alone before. Well, she's never travelled except to Hull and Scarborough on the bus and some short train journeys. The trouble is, that although we have a railway station at Sunkstead, it is two miles out of the village, because people thought that trains would be harmful to humans and animals. So, we usually use the bus. She had, of course, gone to Teddy's house. But that was different because she was with adults all the time.

"Can I borrow your grey case?" she asked.

I took my embroidery out again and carefully put it in a drawer for safe keeping.

I smoothed it out and held each piece. How I loved this, if I could only do one thing, I would choose to embroider.

"Mam, hurry up."

I picked up my case and went to her room.

"I'm going as fast as I can."

"I know, but I need to pack."

It was getting quite late and she had an early start.

"Are you alright, though?"

"Yes, I'm alright, it is marvellous what the doctors can do these days, you know."

"I know."

I asked Herb for the money for her train and £1 for emergencies. Next day she left on the early morning bus, when Herb and I were doing morning milking.

"Why is she going so far away?" I asked Herb when I had washed the buckets and put them in the sterilizer. We walked in for a cup of tea.

"I don't know, love, mebbie it's for the best."

"How can you say that? What's good about our daughter being out of reach? Why doesn't she go to a college in Hull and stay near us like the other two? We will hardly ever see her; she still needs my guidance you know. She doesn't know the half of it. Why is she going to the other side of the world?"

"Now don't get worked up, love, you know that won't be good for your health, will it?" You stay and have another cup of tea." He patted my knees gently and went out to clean the cow shed. I didn't need patting for goodness' sake.

I sat thinking, maybe she would not get in. But if she does, I will not be able to tell her what to do and guide her. Even though she seems to take no notice of me, some of what I say must sink in.

On the whole, it would be better and safer, if she stayed here and married Brian. I could see her every week. I'm sure Sid would drive me to Ripsea or I could go on the bus to see her if Herb didn't want to. Not that I have any say in the matter now – it's all in God's hands.

While she was away, as part of my new health plan, I have decided to go to 'Movement to Music' in the village hall opposite – it's for the over fifties so I just about qualify.

"Who's counting?" asked Peggy She was staying with a friend at Ringam and was even younger than me. She had settled in down south and had come up to Yorkshire on a flying visit. I wish she wasn't so far away but at least she is used to travelling. I think it must be that she travelled so much in the war she has got used to it. She is quite a woman of the world.

There were six women already there at my movement lesson, not counting the teacher. She was a retired PE teacher from a school in Hull, come to live with her elderly mother in Sunkstead. 'Good job I've got Herb,' I thought. 'I can't see my children coming to live with me. I'm not sure I would want them to.'

There was a big gramophone in the corner and some gentle music was already playing. We took our coats off and waited.

"It doesn't look as if anybody else is coming, so let's get started," said Miss Frost.

"Gentle stretches first to warm up, just copy me."

She stood at the front and stretched her arms out above her head and then reached down and touched her toes. I couldn't raise my arms as high, but I could touch my toes and when I was down there, I looked sideways at Doris, next to me, she was a bit too plump and couldn't reach the wooden floor. She started to laugh, and we all joined in. The warm-up was good for me and when we had to move in time to the music, I got into it really well. Miss Frost offered chairs to anybody who couldn't manage.

'Is she talking to me? Does she think I can't do this? I'm not past it yet.' I was furious.

I moved about in time to Mozart, with Peggy next to me. She was very fit and active – she and Henry were always walking great distances.

For some reason, I started to think about the dances at Ringam that Herb and I had gone to – how we waltzed across the floor. My green sequinned dress billowing and my golden dance shoes smoothly gliding. Herb was a good dancer, we could forget about the farm and all the hard work, as we floated off together, arm in arm.

"Half-time everybody, time for a cup of tea and a rest," shouted Miss Frost, looking hot and bothered.

Doris came in from the kitchen puffing and panting with a great big teapot, you could hardly see her head above it. Peggy poured.

"This exercise will be good for you," said Doris.

Does she mean me or is she talking to us all? Does she know I am ill, has she noticed my left finger trembling? I want to look like everybody else. I was determined to do the second half even better, just to show her.

At the end, when we had cleared away, I went with Peggy to the bus stop.

"That was fun; do you think you will go to a class at home?"

I said 'home', but I always thought that her home was here. She was miles away – even further than Birmingham.

At least she didn't say that it would do me good or that I had done well – considering...

"Yes, I think I will."

"The laughing did me good," said Peggy. "Good old Doris, with that teapot," and as she got on the bus she was still laughing, and I laughed as the bus set off.

Sid came the next day.

"How's tricks?"

"Very good."

"I'm pleased about that."

It's true, I was feeling good about last night. I had enjoyed it. It had taken me out of myself and things looked much better today.

"Can't stop, I'm off to a Managers' meeting at Ripsea school. I will be busy there as well as on the farm now. You knew I'd been appointed, didn't you?"

"Herb did say something about it, yes." Herb was out looking after the sheep. I wish he wanted to be a school manager and dress up in a smart suit. But Herb just wanted to work on the farm, and I would have to accept that.

After Sid had gone, I realised that the whispering was coming to an end. Soon all my daughters will have left home and Herb and I will work things out together. I am lucky with Herb; he is strong and steady.

Then I started to wonder how Vi was getting on. Would she find the right train home? What about changing train stations at Manchester? She did not know anything about cities and trains and people who might harm her. In the end, I got so worried I managed to persuade Herb to go in the car with me to pick her up at Paragon station in Hull. He didn't like going at all because he had to get changed and then he would have to change back into his working clothes for milking. But he took me all the same.

"I'm not buying a platform ticket," he said when we were at the gates. "Waste of money."

"But we might miss her – if we go up to the train as it pulls in, we will see her getting off."

"We won't miss her – she has to come through this gate."

Herb saw her first.

"There she is," he shouted pointing his pipe. "I told you she would be alright, didn't I?" He was as relieved as I was.

Chapter 19

The escape

Me

Life settled back down again. I worked at school and revised at home for my exams during the weekend. Not long to go now. I was still going out with Bri and we still went on Saturday night to The Cosy Cinema.

We watched Cliff Richard in the film *The Young Ones*, where young people were fighting a property developer, who wanted the land that their youth club was built on. Cliff sang that we must not be afraid, and he said that we shouldn't wait for tomorrow. He was so right, I didn't want to wait, I wanted to do something important now. I wanted to do something like Cliff did.

I decided to go to the youth club that Bri went to. He had been asking me for ages and now Cliff had pointed the way in his film. Maybe Ripsea Youth Club needed saving by me.

The next Saturday we went. I wore my yellow shirt dress with a thin white belt. Mam had made it for me, it matched her kitchen. I didn't really like it but at least it was short. I made her take the hem up an inch, when she was tacking it. Bri wore his casual slacks and a check shirt. The vicar (who was dressed like Bri but with a dog collar) was running the club and Bri was the treasurer.

We were in the church hall – there were lots of rooms, all more or less empty. Our voices echoed, and I sat down on one of the old wooden chairs round the room – they matched the wooden floor. Bri went to make coffee in the little kitchen – he pushed the mugs through a hatch, and I went to get mine. I don't like coffee, but I drank it, sipping slowly while things 'hotted up' and Bri counted the money.

"Do you want to play table tennis?" asked Bri suddenly – his voice bouncing round the empty room.

"Might as well."

I had often played in our big room at Gum. Our mahogany table was massive and was ideal with the green net we put across the middle. It was great fun.

Now, I played for a bit, on this little youth club folding table, the noise of the ball sounding louder than it really was. Backwards and forwards went the ping pong. The table wasn't big enough and I often hit the ball onto the floor. Bri won and we sat down again.

"Anyone for Coke?" asked the vicar popping up from behind the homemade beige Formica counter, with a lop-sided shelf on the wall behind it.

"Lovely," said Bri, rubbing his hands together and then getting up and bringing us a bottle each – then we had to go back and lever the cap off with a metal thing fixed to the Formica. I had never had this before – we drank it out of the bottle, to save on washing up.

A few more people came, and the vicar put some music on his record player. I recognised the hand jive song and I jived with my hands, like Marcia, but Bri hadn't heard it before.

"Shall we dance?" asked Bri and I got up – we did the jive with our legs for a bit

Nobody else danced so we sat down. Bri had a fag and we played whist.

"Right folks," shouted the vicar "it's nine o'clock, let's all clear up." We swept the floor, wiped the Formica and left.

I went home on the last bus. This boring youth club didn't need saving. Who would want to save it? I never went again.

Anyway, I hadn't really got the time. I had serious revision to do. I went again to Hull library to study on Saturday, now I didn't have to go to a music lesson. I had a big table and as many reference books as I wanted. Chemistry was hard and I had to get it right. I looked up The Northern Matriculation Board,

A level Chemistry syllabus – I wanted to check how far through we were. We were only about halfway! I knew that Veronica's parents had bought her the syllabuses of her subjects and she had a paid tutor to help her. I was on my own. I decided to work on the extra parts of the syllabus myself, as well as working on what we were doing in class.

Just out of interest, and to think about something else for a while, I looked up my childhood illness. It had been caused by teething powder – it poisoned me. I knew that much, and I had been very poorly for a long time – they told me that.

"You had Pink Disease," said Aunty Peggy. "You were very poorly for a long time. You owe your life to your mother."

I found a medical dictionary and looked it up. 'Pink Disease – caused by mercury poisoning in children – now of historic interest – in teething powder.'

Mercury – I was poisoned by mercury, from the teething powder that my mam rubbed on my gums – how was it that Aunty Peggy thought Mam had saved my life? Mam had caused the problem in the first place. I did not understand; nobody had talked to me about this.

I couldn't understand the medical notes either, in any case, I was too frightened to read more. It was all too much to take in. I turned back to my chemistry work.

Sandra met me in Hull sometimes on Saturdays. We sat in a coffee bar and chatted. She was going out with one of the cashiers at the bank, called Paul. The bank didn't like it and moved her boyfriend to another bank in York. You weren't allowed to 'fraternise' with the opposite sex, apparently.

"I'm selling my typewriter," she told me. "I won't need it now."

"Why not?"

"I've decided to give up work, when we get engaged, then Paul can come back and work in Hull. We are going to get married next spring. I'll need the time to get ready."

I saw my chance. "I'll buy the typewriter off you, how much?"

She was a bit taken aback but told me she wanted £5.

"I'll give you four pounds." And so, it was agreed, but I didn't have £4 and had no idea where I would get that much money. I had never been any good at tidy handwriting, like Mam is, and I thought that a typewriter would be good for making notes.

I talked to Mam and Dad about my good idea of buying Sandra's typewriter. I didn't say I had already agreed to buy it and one morning Dad handed me £4 – four new £1 notes.

It was mine – a little portable Olivetti in a blue zip case with a snazzy black stripe. I hadn't done any lessons in typing, but how hard could it be? Quite hard, as it turned out. I borrowed a book from the library called *Learn to Type in Two Weeks*. It took me a bit longer than that, but I did learn. I typed out all my notes for revision.

Next, I needed a watch for the exams. Our Katy and Gwendy were bought watches when they went nursing. They were proper nursing watches and, of course, were a must. I didn't have to have one, but what if the clock was too far away in the gym, where we did our exams. Or what if it stopped or was wrong?

"You could borrow my gold watch," Mam offered.

"What? That old thing. It doesn't even keep time. It's no good to me."

In the end Mam and Dad took me into the jewellers in Ripsea and there were five watches to choose from on a piece of cream velvet. I chose one – the cheapest, and the one with the clearest dials.

I sat my A levels. I felt sick.

'All life depends ultimately on the sun, discuss.' I know that this is about plants making food in the sunlight. This was the start of the botany exam. But it was a third of the marks, so it wasn't going to be a simple answer.

'How are multi-celled and single celled animals different and how are they similar?' This is about life processes. This was zoology.

'Explain the significance of the first chapter in the gospel according to Saint Matthew.'

I knew about this. I knew about Matthew and who he was writing to. I was good at the Bible I had got my own way, after all, and I had taken RE as one of my subjects.

Before my last chemistry paper, I really was sick, I mean actually sick. Mr Boyes came. He sat with me on the bench next to the showers. He was holding the bowl. My boiled breakfast egg came back.

"You cannot go in more than twenty minutes after the start."

I took some deep breaths. What was he doing here anyway? He wasn't my chemistry teacher.

"Why are you here?"

"Miss Legg saw you outside the examination room and came running, asking if anyone could help. I came because I know you and even though I have not taught girls before, I thought I may be able to persuade you." He looked over his rimless glasses at me. His grey eyes were piercing and urging me on. Even though he had not taught girls before – he knew about me. He held the bowl and I retched again. There was nothing more in my stomach.

"This is your last exam. Go in, go in. Please go in."

But I couldn't, I just couldn't. I am never going to put myself through this again.

I went in. I walked to my desk and turned the paper. I looked at my watch, divided the time for the questions and I began.

It was all over.

I went to see Bri and this time, I was allowed in his bedroom. This had never happened before. We always sat with his parents, but now it was different, for some reason.

"Do you want to see my new fish tank? I have some zebra and neon fish and some guppies." I followed him up the winding stairs.

The fish were beautiful, I could see why he liked them. We sat on his bed watching them swimming in and out of the weed and little ornaments that Bri had carefully placed there. He really was a nice person. Then I saw a little red seaside bucket and it was nearly full of six- penny pieces.

"What's that for?"

"It's my seaside bucket, from when I was little."

"Why are there sixpences in it?"

"For our engagement ring."

"What?"

"I'm saving for your ring."

I stumbled down the stairs and rushed down the road and onto the bus.

Next morning, I heard the letter box bang. When would somebody finally get round to oiling it?

Mam brought the letter to me.

"Your letter is here with a Birmingham postmark."

I didn't open my eyes.

"Is it thick or thin?"

"Thick."

"I've got in then." I smiled under the covers.

Mam went downstairs, leaving me my mug of tea, but I didn't drink it. I went back to sleep. An hour later I opened my eyes, there was a postcard from Marcia next to my Birmingham letter.

'I didn't get in,' so they must have told the ones who they were refusing first, 'I don't care! I'm going to France with Mike.' Mike? I thought it was Marty.

The letter and prospectus told me all the things I needed to buy, and Mam was soon off to her Hull saleroom to get a trunk – the other things like a car rug and smart dress she got for me from Katy's catalogue. I had to have a smart jacket as well. I really hoped she would not make one. The letter also said that I had to have a medical. I had to go to a clinic just off Kingston Square in Hull. I wasn't worried because I had just had a health check with Doctor Newby, in any case I had other things on my mind.

I had to tell Bri. But what could I say?

"It's not your fault – it's mine."

I needed to get away, being with him meant staying, getting married and living at Ripsea. That can't be what my life is about. Surely not? There has to be more – I am going to look for it.

My A level results came quite quickly in the summer holidays. They were just what I needed. I had passed with the grades I wanted. They were even good enough for university, but I was going to college. Mam was over the moon and rang Veronica's mam straight away. Then she was at the saleroom in Hull again.

She bought an awful brown trunk, for me to send to college. Why couldn't I have a new one? Everybody else would have a new one, but I had to have an ancient saleroom one. I couldn't believe it when Dad brought it back in our van. It was old, like something from the attic at my great-aunties' house. It had bamboo strips round it and inside it was lined with cream cotton cloth. I could hardly bear to look at it, never mind touch it. You could smell mothballs a mile away.

Mam sent my brown trunk, with bamboo strips round it, ahead of me with British Road.

The pig skin case was from the saleroom as well, and it was nearly as bad. It was a great big expander and was scruffy, but it would have to do – it was all I had. I packed my case with my clothes.

You were supposed to have a dressing gown and slippers, but I hadn't got any and didn't think Mam would want to spend any more. I had bought a sponge bag, so I would not be the only person without one this time. I put a toothbrush in and some hand cream, but I had been so busy with my school work, I hadn't had time to buy new eye make-up and things like that. I had a lipstick though, and a hair brush. My books were ordered from the college booklist and were waiting for me in Birmingham.

Amy sent me a Good Luck card – 'I'll look after Bri for you' – she wrote – 'I am working at the chemist in Ripsea now.' I can imagine what she thought of me – what everybody thought of me, but I was on a journey that I couldn't stop. Amy and Bri would be good together.

I looked round my room, with the bedspread made by Mam and the mirror from the saleroom that needed 're-silvering'. I held my sunrise shell and felt the ridges with my fingers, I looked at the pink coming up from the pointed end and wondered how it could be so lovely. Then I wrapped my precious shell up, in some greaseproof paper from Mam's yellow kitchen, and put it safely in my pocket.

On the day that I left home, I took the little parcel out of my pocket and wrote 'Mam' on it. I looked at it, then I added a kiss 'X'. I put it on the old bedside cabinet that just needed some sanding to make it as good as new.

I dragged my big pig-skin case to the door with one hand. The handle pressed into my palm and made a red mark. I tried to hold onto my typewriter and my record player in the other hand, but it was impossible.

I put everything down and opened the case. I took some clothes out. I wouldn't need that many clothes, would I? I especially didn't want the ones made my mam, I would look so old-fashioned. I kept my C&A skirt, though, and my red sheath dress. Now, there was enough room for my typewriter in my suitcase. I snapped the case shut again.

The prospectus says all assignments must be handwritten, I can't think why, wait till they see my handwriting. But even if they do want everything in my handwriting, I can still type all my notes. I can file them, and they will be easy to refer to, for study purposes. I really had to take my typewriter. And I really had to take my Dansette, I needed to hear Buddy Holly.

I held my case with the metal handle in one hand, and my Dansette with the other. The deep blue cover was like the clear morning sky. It was just before seven o'clock.

Mam and Dad were milking the cows when I left, banging the big front door, with its letter box that still hadn't been oiled. Nobody said 'Goodbye, good luck'. I just crashed out of their lives. I went to the bus stop, lugging my case.

They didn't care that I was going – the farm came first. I stood in the wooden shelter waiting for the Hull bus to come. I got on the bus and heaved my pig-skin case into the storage hole under the stairs.

I glanced back, just once. A sob rose in my throat, then I turned and faced the front to look at the driver, who was staring ahead of him.

The engine breathed into life, the gears grating. The bus dragged away, heaving me out of the thick brown mud of Sunkstead and on to Hull and to the rest of the world.

Mam

I could not believe it when I saw the list of things she needed to buy for college. It all seems quite posh. For one thing she has to have a car rug. Well, that can only mean one thing – she will be going on outings – maybe at some distance. I ordered that from Katy's catalogue. She had to have a cup and saucer and plate, but we didn't need to buy new – she could get these from the kitchen. The list seemed endless, I left it up to her to pack the rest.

Who would have thought it? My third girl going off to college. The sickly one – the one that was poisoned by accident, because the manufacturers hadn't checked enough. How was I to know? I still ask myself. It was all their fault.

There was a long book list they added up to £35, it seemed like an outrageous amount.

"I'll give her the money for her books, I want her to have the best," said Herb – he seems to have really got into all this college business.

"I thought you said book learning was no good," I reminded him of what he had often said.

"Aye, but I can see she set her mind on study. She's always up in her room reading her books and seems to be working hard – if you can call book learning hard work." He couldn't help adding that last bit.

There were a lot of questions – which would be the best books, but what do I know? Vi chose them, and the order and cheque, signed by Herb, went off to a bookshop in Birmingham. They would deliver to the college.

Another thing on the list was a trunk. I decided to try my luck at the saleroom in Hull again. I still love going there. I had to go quite a few times before I saw a trunk. It was an old one but in perfect condition – just the job. I held my card up and kept it there, I was going to have this. I made sure that I sat at the front so that even though I could not hold my card high up, the auctioneer could still see me. I sat through chairs and tables and couches being sold, then it was 'this very fine trunk, in good condition worth ten shillings of anybody's money'. I had to have that trunk – my heart was beating fast. Somebody else wanted it – oh no! I could see the auctioneer looking behind me and taking a bid of two shillings. I held my card steady for the next bid.

"I am bid two shillings and six pence for this fine trunk. A piece of history, still plenty of use in it – cheap at the price."

I held firm.

"Gone for two-shillings-six-pence to the lady at the front."

It was mine. And my luck stayed with me because now there was a pig-skin suitcase going under the hammer. I got it cheaply, it was a bit scuffed but just what Vi needed.

I made sure a smart jacket was packed in the trunk, I made it myself to a traditional design from my mother's patterns. She would look posh on those trips. I tailored it, just like we used to and, though I say it myself, it does look stylish. I packed the woollen car rug. I put an old jumper in that had belonged to Gwendy.

British Road Services came to collect it in good time – it would take about a fortnight to get to college. I suppose it had to go to all the depots and wait to be picked up for the next leg of its journey.

"How is she going to live, Herb?"

"Like we do, I would think."

"I mean what is she going to do for money?"

"She won't need much, she gets full board and lodging."

"But she will need some cash for little personal extras, you know."

"We'll have to send her some money then. But she needs to know that money doesn't grow on trees. We wouldn't be where we are now if we'd kept on spending all the time."

"What do you think we should send, a pound a week?"

"That sounds about right."

"Thank you, Herb."

I worked out that I could send her a pound note inside my copy of *Woman's Weekly*, when I had read it. I'd already been to the Post Office and found out that you can buy brown wrappers to put the address on, then you stick it round a magazine and that is cheaper than sending in an envelope. I can put a letter in as well as the pound note, at no extra cost. I will enjoy writing her a letter every week. I like writing and I can tell her how we are doing on the farm.

"How will she get home? She won't have money for the train fare back at Christmas." I am thinking ahead and organising.

"Mebbie I'll set up a bank account for her. Aye, next time I go to my bank in Hull, I'll get them to sort it out for her. Then I can put train ticket money in there."

"Can we phone you, Vi?" I asked that night.

"Yes, if you want, I saw in their prospectus that there is a phone for public use in the Hall of Residence."

"I'll phone you once a week then, can you give me the number?" I was trying to hang on to her life, have some influence, some control. I wrote the number down.

"I'll phone at six o'clock every Saturday night." She didn't answer.

"Is that alright?"

"Yes."

"Make sure you are near the phone then."

We had the letter just before she left. It was from the College Principal. At the top it said – *'Bedroom visits by the opposite sex'*.

'As you know our Halls of Residence are, of necessity, single sex dwellings. Each residence has a Matron and a Cook and a Warden living in. In the case of male residences, the Warden will be male otherwise all officers in the halls are female.

In these modern times, there has been some talk about allowing opposite sexes to visit students' rooms. May I remind you that these rooms are essentially bedrooms. Suitable visiting accommodation is provided by way of a supervised common room in each hall.

We are mindful of the partnership we hold with you in caring for the well-being of your daughter...'

Me and Herb read the letter together when we were alone. We had to answer at the end –

' YES, I want my daughter to have members of the opposite sex in her bedroom.

NO, I do not want my daughter to have members of the opposite sex in her bedroom.

Circle YES or NO.

Please return in envelope provided.'

"It's NO."

"Aye."

"I hope she's careful. I'm not sure she knows all about the dangers out there. They are not all as good and safe as Brian."

"She comes from a good home and I'm sure she knows what's what. Now where's our pen, I'll ring that 'NO'."

"We won't say anything to her. It's addressed to us after all."

She's leaving this morning — going on the early bus.

I went out with Herb to do morning milking. I washed udders and put clusters on. Herb set the machines going. We heard again, the pulse of the electric milking. I was thinking about my last daughter to leave. Gwendy and Katy have done well, they have good careers which they can always fall back on. They have good husbands and we have one grandchild. Vi will get there in the end. They are all a little bit like me, a little bit like Herb and a little bit like themselves — too much like herself in the case of Vi.

Good heavens — is that the time?

I just popped in to look at the clock, I do not wear my gold watch for working outside. It only seemed like a minute since I went out and now it is seven o'clock. Drat! Vi will have gone.

No time to take my milking coat off, I can't worry about what people will think now. I dash out leaving the front door open — I must oil that letter box when I have a minute. Now I am concentrating on trying to get to the end of our side road where it meets the main road.

Oh! There's the bus at the stop. I can see it in the distance.

'Run, legs, run. Keep going, one foot in front of the other, like in the war, like we've always done.'

They won't run, they won't do what I am telling them to do. The people are getting on the bus.

"Run," I shout. "Run, you stupid legs."

But my legs are beyond my command now, and it's as if I am struggling through thick mud. I push all my energy down to my feet, until I am at the end of our road, at last. I can see the back of the bus — everybody has got on and it is pulling away.

Me and my Mam

I am too late. I watch helplessly. She has gone. My daughter has gone.

I try to wave – but my right hand will not go above my head. My elbow is still bent. I push my left hand against it, and it straightens and lifts. With one hand held up high I wave to the disappearing bus carrying my daughter.

Me

When I look back through that bus window, I see her standing at the end of our road wearing her brown milking coat and wellies. My mam has one hand held up high – and she is waving to me.

That's my mam.

* * *

194

Vicky Turrell

Vicky grew up on a farm in East Yorkshire. She left home to train as a teacher and specialise in science. She then graduated from the Open University. Vicky was a science advisory teacher for Shropshire and Telford before becoming a Headteacher.

She now lives on a smallholding in Shropshire and has written two books based on her fortnightly column for the *Oswestry and Border Counties Advertizer*.

'Me and my Mam' is the sequel to Vicky's first book 'It's not a Boy!'

Also by Vicky Turrell

It's Not A Boy!
Vicky Turrell

.

"It's not a boy!" shouted Posty as he carried the sad news round the scattered houses in the little village of Gum. He was used to bringing bad news in the war and saw no reason to stop.

A girl had been born to a farming family who really wanted a boy. This is the voice of that little girl, now eleven years old, telling her story.

Brought up on a remote farm in Yorkshire in the 1940s and '50s, she shows how her birth was a bombshell to her farming parents.

Living in rural isolation, she saw and interpreted, in her own inexperienced way, all aspects of human life.

To make up for not being a boy she devised a list of things she was good at so that she could succeed and make her parents proud of her. But is her list good enough?

This story was inspired by real events although some scenes and people have been invented for the purpose of the narrative. The language used is of its time.

Purchase from www.leafbyleafpress.com

A Kindle digital version is also available in the Kindle Amazon store.

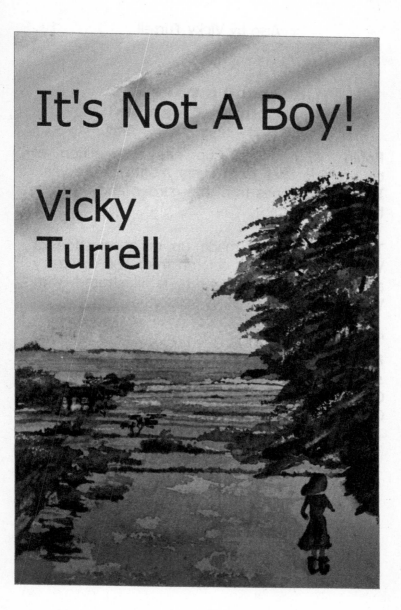

It's Not A Boy!

Vicky Turrell

Also by Vicky Turrell

Robin on my Tea cup
A Country Calendar

Robin on my Tea Cup has a selection of countryside tales from every month of the year. It tells the stories from the garden and fields as the year goes by.

This little book is made up of a selection of Vicky's Nature Notes column from The Oswestry and Borders Advertizer. It is illustrated with Vicky's photos from every season

'...turning to Vicky's column is like a summer breeze gently smoothing out the stresses and strains...'
Colin Channon, Editor,
Oswestry and Borders Advertizer.

Purchase from www.leafbyleafpress.com

Robin on my Tea Cup
A Country Calendar

By Vicky Turrell

Also by Vicky Turrell

Ducklings on my Doorstep
Nature Notes

The countryside in words and picture through the months. Ducklings on my Doorstep is the second collection of Vicky's ever popular *Nature Notes* column included every other week in the Oswestry and Border Counties Advertizer.

'... readers can count on Vicky's columns to provide a refreshing jaunt through the area's wonderful rural spaces.'
Geraint Jones, Head of News,
Oswestry and Borders Advertizer.

Purchase from www.leafbyleafpress.com

Ducklings on my Doorstep
By Vicky Turrell

Nature Notes